Ge

C000183641

by Allan Inso. .... Daisy and Andy Gale

Edited by
J. T. Greensmith

ISBN 0-900717-54-8

The Isle of Wight

CONTENTS

The Isle of Wight

PREFACE

The Isle of Wight has attracted amateur and professional geologists since Webster published the first account of its coastal exposures (in Englefield, 1816). No other area of comparable size in England has such a variety of formations in easily accessible exposures and containing such a diversity and abundance of fossils. Within its small area, the island provides a near-complete early Cretaceous to mid-Palaeogene succession, unrivalled elsewhere in western Europe.

The purpose of this field guide is twofold: firstly, to provide a general introduction to the island's geology and secondly to provide descriptive accounts of locations which can be visited to see this geology.

The majority of the localities described are readily accessible both by road and the coastal footpath. The itineraries are arranged in a clockwise sequence around the island beginning in the northeast. If time is limited, it is suggested that Whitecliff Bay, Sandown Bay, Chale Bay, Hanover Point and Alum Bay are the most important sites. The small but excellent Museum of Isle of Wight Geology, High Street, Sandown should also be visited.

A useful general account of the area within a broader regional context can be found in the British Regional Guide to the Hampshire Basin (Melville & Freshney, 1982). There is no modern detailed account of the geology of the Isle of Wight, although White (1921) provides a useful though somewhat dated stratigraphical description.

The Isle of Wight is covered by Ordnance Survey 1:50,000 sheet 196 and 1:250,000 Outdoor Leisure Map 29. The relevant geological map is the Geological Survey 1:50,000 Isle of Wight Special Sheet. Visitors will also find the British Geological Survey *Isle of Wight Holiday Guide* useful. Throughout this guide, wherever National Grid References are quoted in the text, the prefix SZ has been omitted. The Isle of Wight has a comprehensive and well-waymarked system of pathways. The county numbering system has been used when appropriate where paths are mentioned in the text.

The island is an important source of fossils and has some of the richest fossil collecting locations in Britain. The small size of the island and its geological resources are finite. In recent years, the growing numbers of collectors has increased pressure on some sites. It is essential that all visitors adopt a responsible attitude and help preserve the unique geological heritage of the Isle of Wight. The Isle of Wight Council has produced a useful booklet entitled *Guidelines for Collecting Fossils on the Isle of Wight* which is available from the

The Isle of Wight

Museum of Isle of Wight Geology in Sandown which, as the title suggests, provides basic information for fossil collectors and should be required reading for all visitors who have come to see the Island's geology.

The authors would like to record their thanks to all those colleagues who have contributed freely of their time and knowledge over the years. The figures were drawn by Bill Johnson and Rosemary Shearer of the Department of Geography, University of Portsmouth. The authors would like to express their thanks to the Faculty of Science, University of Portsmouth, for a contribution towards the cost of producing this publication.

The Geologists' Association wishes to acknowledge the financial support of the Nature Conservancy Council for England and Enterprise Oil plc.

The Isle of Wight

LIST OF FIGURES

The Isle of Wight

INTRODUCTION

The Isle of Wight forms part of the geological structure known as the Wessex-Channel Basin. A geological succession of early Cretaceous to early Oligocene age is exposed below some remnant Pleistocene cover (Figure 1). The oldest rocks are brought to the surface in the cores of two asymmetrical anticlines, the Brighstone Anticline in the west and the Sandown Anticline in the east (Figure 2). The southern limbs of both folds dip relatively gently southwards but the northern limbs are much steeper and in places vertical, and hence the overall structure is often referred to as the Isle of Wight Monocline.

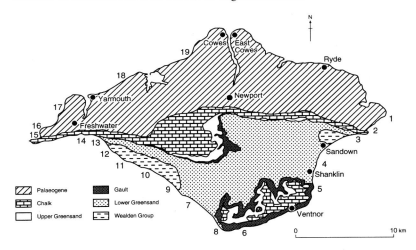

Figure 1. Outline geological map of the Isle of Wight.

CRETACEOUS

Introduction

The Cretaceous rocks which crop out in the southern half of the island preserve an almost unbroken stratigraphic sequence from the Wealden Group to the Upper Chalk, within which ten formations are recognised (Tables 1 & 2). The stratigraphic nomenclature used is after Daley & Stewart (1979), Gale, Wood & Bromley (1987), Simpson (1985) and Wach & Ruffell (1991). The succession can be examined in the magnificent coastal sections between Sandown Bay and The Needles (Itineraries 3 to 14).

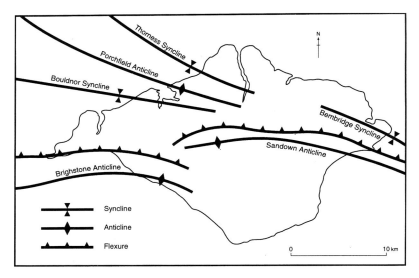

Figure 2. Structural geology of the Isle of Wight.

Wealden Group

The Wealden Group crops out in two areas on the Isle of Wight (Figure 1): a small area within the core of the Sandown Anticline (Itinerary 3) and a larger one on the southwest coast in the core of the Brighstone Anticline (Itineraries 9 to 12). In both areas, the Wealden Group can be subdivided into two units: Wessex Formation (formerly Wealden Marls) and Vectis Formation (formerly Wealden Shales) (Daley & Stewart, 1979; Stewart, 1981a). The maximum outcrop thickness of the Wealden Group is about 240 m, but the Arreton 1 Well proved a total thickness of about 580 m for the unit (Falcon & Kent, 1960). However, geophysical evidence indicates that, north of the Isle of Wight Monocline, the Wealden Group is either absent or poorly developed (Allen & Holloway, 1984; Chadwick 1985b).

The **Wessex Formation** has a maximum visible thickness of about 180 m. It is a nonmarine sequence comprising varicoloured, but mainly red, mudstones with subordinate sandstones. The sedimentology has been described by Daley & Stewart (1979), Stewart (1981a, b) and Insole & Hutt (1994). The mudstones represent the vertical accretion of suspended load from ponded flood waters on an alluvial plain. Some mudstone or interbedded mudstone-sandstone sequences infill recognisable channels and were laid down by vertical accretion of

Wealden

GROUP	FORMATION	MEMBER	STAGE
	Upper Greensand		Albian
	Gault		
	Carstone		
Lower Greensand	Sandrock		
	Ferruginous Sands	Members XIV & XV	Aptian
		New Walpen Chine Member	
		Old Walpen Chine Member	
		Member XI	
		Member X	
		Ladder Chine Member	
		Member VIII	
		Whale Chine Member	
		Member VI	
		Member V	
		Member IV	
	Atherfield Clay	Upper Lobster Bed	
		Crackers	
		Lower Lobster Bed	
		Chale Clay	
		Perna Bed	
Wealden	Vectis	Shepherd's Chine	Barremian
		Barnes High Sandstone	
		Cowleaze Chine	
	Wessex		

TABLE 1. Stratigraphy of the Lower Cretaceous sequence on the Isle of Wight.

suspended load from flood waters trapped in abandoned chute or cut-off channels. The colour mottling, which is such a conspicuous feature of the mudstones within the Wessex Formation, was caused by post-depositional diagenesis, mainly due to pedogenic (soil-forming) processes.

Most of the sandstones within the formation are fining-upward units of conglomerates, sandstones, siltstones and mudstones. Above an erosional base, these units exhibit a general change from large-scale trough or planar cross-bedding, through flat bedding, climbing ripple lamination or small-scale cross-bedding to interbedded sands and muds. Within each sandstone body there is often considerable lateral variation. Some of the units are actually multiple and consist of several distinct sand bodies separated from each other by erosion surfaces. Fining-upward units of this type were deposited as channel lags, point bars and levees within the meander belt of stream channels. Some units within the formation comprise fine-grained sandstones, siltstones and mudstones organised into laterally accreted fining-upward sequences. These were deposited as muddy point bars by high sinuosity streams bearing mainly suspended loads (Stewart, 1983). On the other hand, small-scale alternations of fine-grained sandstone and red mudstone represent crevasse channel fills and crevasse splays, with successive floods laying down a succession of sand-mud couplets.

GROUP	FORMATION	MEMBER	STAGE
Chalk	White Chalk		Maastrichtian
		Studland	Campanian
		Portsdown	
		Culver	
		Newhaven	Santonian
		Broadstairs	Coniacian
		St. Margaret's	Turonian
		Ranscombe	
	Lower Chalk	Plenus Marls	Cenomanian
		Grey Chalk	
		Chalk Marl	
		Glauconitic Marl	
	Upper Greensand		Albian

TABLE 2. Stratigraphy of the Upper Cretaceous sequence on the Isle of Wight.

Wealden

Scattered irregularly throughout the Wessex Formation are units comprising grey silty or sandy clays packed with plant debris, including in many cases large logs. This distinctive lithology occurs in thin, sometimes lenticular beds. Much of the plant debris in these units is in the form of fusain (fossil charcoal), indicating that occasional brush fires occurred on the alluvial plain. These plant debris beds are the main source of fossils within the Wessex Formation, yielding not only plant material but also fish teeth and scales, crocodile, turtle and dinosaur bones. Nearly all the vertebrate material is disarticulated and the dinosaur bones are usually rolled and broken. The plant debris beds were deposited by local intrabasinal and interfluvial flood/debris flow events.

The geomorphic setting in which Wessex Formation deposition took place comprised a perennial, moderately sized, high sinuosity river flowing across a low-relief alluvial plain within a relatively narrow fault-bounded, E-W oriented valley (Insole & Hutt, 1994). Deposition within the river valley generally consisted of extrabasinal sediment laid down in channel, point bar and floodplain environments. Palaeocurrent, petrographic and heavy mineral data indicates sediment derivation from the Breton-Cornubian Massif to the west. The river carried a dominant suspension load with little or no bed load and this led to the development of muddy point bars. At times, the bed load increased, probably in response to climatic events in the hinterland. During these flood events, sandy point bars were formed. It appears that lakes and/or ponds occurred locally on the floodplain, but they were commonly temporary features and frequently dried out. Some areas of the alluvial plain were sediment-starved for sufficiently long intervals of time for pedogenesis (soil formation) and calcrete formation to occur. The occurrence of calcretes (calcium carbonate precipitated within a soil) indicates that deposition took place in a warm climate with a sparse and seasonal rainfall. Times of relative dryness are also reflected by the intercalation of muds within the sandy point bars suggesting a periodic, marked reduction of water throughput.

The **Vectis Formation** consists mainly of dark grey siltstones and mudstones. The contact with the underlying Wessex Formation is marked by an abrupt colour change from red to grey. The upper boundary is marked by an eroded and burrowed contact with the basal glauconitic sandstone (Perna Bed Member) of the succeeding Atherfield Clay Formation (Lower Greensand Group). The maximum thickness of the formation is about 66 m. The Vectis Formation sequence is subdivided into three members: Cowleaze Chine, Barnes High Sandstone and Shepherd's Chine Members (Daley & Stewart, 1979; Stewart, 1981b).

The basal **Cowleaze Chine Member** comprises mainly finely interlaminated dark grey mudstone and pale grey silt/fine-grained sand, sometimes arranged in relatively thin fining-upward units. The mudstones are frequently intensely

Wealden

bioturbated. In some areas, an approximately 1 m thick white fine sand (the "White Rock") occurs at the base of the member. Faunal assemblages within this member are dominated by forms such as the gastropod *Viviparus* and the bivalves *Filosina* and, less commonly, *Unio,* indicating freshwater or slightly brackish salinity conditions. The laminated mudstones are considered to have been deposited in a shallow brackish water lagoon/mudflat environment (Stewart *et al.,* 1991; Wach & Ruffell, 1991).

The Cowleaze Chine Member is overlain by the **Barnes High Sandstone Member** which consists of one or more relatively thick yellow to grey sandstone units. The contact with the Cowleaze Chine Member is variable in character: at some localities, it is an abrupt lithological change, while at others it is gradational. For convenience the boundary is placed at the base of the first medium-grained yellow sand, whether this is in the form of a continuous bed or a discontinuous lenticular layer. In Sandown and Brighstone Bays (Itineraries 3 and 9) the Barnes High Sandstone consists of a single coarsening-upward sandstone unit, but in Compton Bay (Itinerary 12) the member comprises three separate sandstones separated by laminated mudstones. In each sandstone unit within the Barnes High Sandstone, there is an upwards decrease in clay content and bedding changes from lenticular to wavy. In the upper part of the member, large-scale cross-bedding and channelling appear. *Ophiomorpha*-like burrows occur within some of the cross-bedded sandstones. The very top of the Barnes High Sandstone may consist of a thin conglomerate comprising mud clasts and the bivalves *Unio* and *Filosina.* A number of possible depositional environments have been suggested for this sand body including tidal sand flats, barrier bar, lagoonal delta and river mouth bar (Stewart, 1978b). The current view is that it was deposited on a prograding lagoonal delta which was subject to some reworking by wave action at the shoreline (Stewart *et al.,* 1991; Wach & Ruffell, 1991).

The succeeding **Shepherd's Chine Member** rests on a sharp, although irregular, top of the Barnes High Sandstone. It consists mainly of rhythmically bedded, grey fine-grained sands, silts and mudstones. Altogether, about 65 relatively thin fining-upward units can be distinguished. Each commences with light grey fine-grained sand or silt and passes up into dark grey mud. The base of each unit is sharp and usually demonstrably erosional. In the lower part of each unit, bands and lenses of flat- and small-scale cross-laminated fine-grained sands occur; these decrease in thickness and frequency upwards. This part of many of the units is also characterised by the presence of steep-sided, sinuous scours (gutter scours) infilled by laminated fine sand. In the higher parts of the Shepherd's Chine Member, there are several thin muddy limestones comprising bivalve shells and shell fragment concentrates. Most contain the bivalve *Filosina* but one near the top of the member contains *Ostrea.* Faunal and microfloral assemblages indicate that, while there was an overall upward increase in salinity, there were

Lower Greensand

fluctuations (Ruffell, 1988; Radley 1995). The Shepherd's Chine Member is interpreted the deposit of a shallow, storm-influenced lagoon (Stewart *et al.*, 1991). The cyclicity probably records intermittent flood events which resulted in increased fluvial input into the lagoon and may reflect a continuation of the climatic fluctuation postulated to have occurred during the deposition of the Wessex Formation.

Lower Greensand Group

The Lower Greensand Group underlies the greater part of the southern half of the island and magnificent exposures can be seen in the coastal cliffs of Sandown Bay (Itineraries 3, 4 & 5), Chale Bay (Itinerary 7) and Compton Bay (Itinerary 13). The Lower Greensand Group succession was deposited under mainly marine conditions, the base representing a marked environmental change with an important marine transgression. The sequence records a succession of periods of rising, static and falling sea-levels.

The lithostratigraphy of the Lower Greensand of the Isle of Wight was first described by Fitton (1847). In Chale Bay (Itinerary 7), which has since become the type section of the group, Fitton recognised 6 divisions, 16 "groups" and 55 beds. Bristow *et al.* (1889) simplified Fitton's stratigraphic scheme by dividing the group into four formations which can be recognised in all the available exposures: Atherfield Clay, Ferruginous Sands, Sandrock and Carstone in ascending order. More recently, Simpson (1985) revised the lithostratigraphy of the Atherfield Clay Formation and Fitton's "groups" have become regarded as members (Wach & Ruffell, 1991) (Table 2). Casey's (1961) definition of Aptian/Albian ammonite zonation was based on research on the Chale Bay section.

The **Atherfield Clay Formation** contains five members (Simpson, 1985). The **Perna Bed Member,** which can be recognised in all sections, overlies a scoured and burrowed surface of the Vectis Formation. This erosion surface represents an important transgressive event of latest Barremian (*bidentatum zone, c.*113·5 Ma) or earliest Aptian (*fissicostatus zone, c.*112 Ma) age or possibly an amalgamation of both (Wach & Ruffell, 1991). The member contains a number of beds, the basal one being the thin, discontinuous Atherfield Bone and Grit Bed (Simpson, 1985), a poorly sorted muddy sand containing derived fish and reptile bone fragments. This represents a transgressive lag. Above this come a number of beds of grey-green and green glauconitic, poorly sorted, muddy sands. Primary sedimentary structures in these beds have generally been destroyed by extensive bioturbation but occasional lenses of small-scale cross-bedded, fine to medium sand occur. Some of these sands are very fossiliferous with a range of oysters and other bivalves, serpulid worm tubes and corals, together with derived fossils including phosphatised Kimmeridgian (Late Jurassic) ammonites. Many of the fossils are broken and/or abraded, although transport distances were probably not great. In general terms, the Perna Bed Member represents a shallow marine shelf environment. Sedimentation rates were sufficiently slow to allow extensive bioturbation by infaunal organisms to take place. However, there was evidently some storm reworking during which scouring and winnowing concentrated both epifaunal and infaunal organisms. Several of the beds exhibit calcareous cement and are capped by a lag of large oyster (*Aetostreon*) accumulations or contain an ichnofauna including the crustacean burrow network *Thalassinoides*. These features indicate the development of firmgrounds, that is relatively permanent firm substrates (Wach & Ruffell, 1991).

Above the Perna Bed, the remainder of the Atherfield Clay Formation comprises a sequence of brown-grey silty muds, silts and fine sands. Part of the unit exhibits coarsening-upward units, some of which are capped by firmgrounds. Sedimentary structures are rare but include isolated wave ripples, gutter casts filled with cross-laminated silt, scoured surfaces and some soft sediment deformation. There are also scattered bands of phosphatic and calcareous concretions. These concretions are usually relatively small but in the Chale Bay section (Itinerary 7) two horizons of large calcareous concretions occur. In Chale Bay, the Atherfield Clay Formation above the basal Perna Bed can be subdivided into **Chale Clay, Lower Lobster Bed, The Crackers** and **Upper Lobster Bed Members,** but elsewhere the formation is more uniform in character and cannot be subdivided so easily, although a sandy interval at Red Cliff probably represents the Crackers Member (Simpson, 1985). The unit contains few body fossils, except in Chale Bay where it contains a relatively abundant fauna of crustaceans and bivalves at some levels. Overall, indications are that the Atherfield Clay Formation was laid down in shallow marine shelf environment, although microfossil evidence indicates that there were some freshwater influences (Crittenden, 1983; Lord & Bown, 1987). Deposition generally took place below wave base but intermittent storm activity caused winnowing and localised scouring.

The Atherfield Clay is overlain without any apparent break by a thick sequence of alternating dark silty clays and muddy glauconitic sands, the **Ferruginous Sands Formation.** The base of the formation is marked by a rapid change from muds to sands and muddy sands. In Chale Bay (Itinerary 7) the Ferruginous Sands Formation is about 134 m thick and is subdivided into eleven members (Table 1), although some of the distinctions are not immediately obvious. Elsewhere, the succession is much thinner and many of the subdivisions cannot be recognised.

The Ferruginous Sands succession broadly comprises a number of coarsening-upward units, dark grey sandy muds or muddy sands passing up into fine to medium, grey-green glauconitic sands. In most of the cliff sections, the

Lower Greensand

glauconite in the sands has been subject to chemical weathering, resulting in the production of iron oxides, hydroxides and carbonates. Hence, the sands generally exhibit a reddish brown to yellow colour and it is only where fresh surfaces are exposed that the unaltered green colour of glauconite can seen. The lower muddy part of each unit represents relatively slow sedimentation. The siltier and sandier upper part of the units reflects increasing currents. Finally, currents increased sufficiently to cause erosion and winnowing, resulting in very slow or non-deposition. In the upper part of many of the units, there was often some degree of cementation of the sediment, leading to the formation of firmgrounds. The discontinuous cementation produces bands of concretions, some of them being relatively large. The concretions may be calcareous, phosphatic or pyritic and are a major source of fossils within the formation. The scoured surfaces of the firmgrounds may be overlain either by the remains of firm substrate epifaunal organisms, the large oyster *Aetostreon* being especially common, and/or a lag of derived fossils. Body fossils are not generally distributed but are restricted to the upper parts of the coarsening-upward units. Bioturbation is ubiquitous and very few primary sedimentary structures have been preserved.

There is no published detailed study of the sedimentology of the Ferruginous Sands. Some observations and conclusions were provided by Nio (1976), using unpublished data from Dike (1972a), who suggested that the sands in the sequence were deposited as marine sand waves, the muddier parts of the sequence representing the intervening troughs. Wach & Ruffell (1991) concluded that the increased sorting and coarsening-upward units reflect shallowing of the shelf probably related to decrease in relative sea-level. They suggested that the cause of the rhythmicity could be changes in sea-level or climatic.

The **Sandrock Formation** succession comprises a number of coarsening-upward units between 15 and 30 m thick. Each unit rests on a scoured surface which may be immediately overlain by a pebble lag. At the base of each unit is a mixture of massive, bioturbated, dark grey to black, often glauconitic muds and finely laminated pale fine-grained sands and dark grey to black muds. These horizons contain a brackish microfauna and are interpreted as estuarine mud fill or tidal flat deposits. The basal muds pass gradationally up through silty sands into well-sorted, fine to coarse quartz sands. There is a general increase in bed thickness and grain size up the unit. The sands exhibit a variety of sedimentary structures including small- to large-scale tabular, trough and, less commonly, herringbone cross-bedding. Individual sets are separated by black mud laminae and mud-draped foresets also occur. Trace fossils, including *Ophiomorpha, Arenicolites* and bivalve escape structures, are abundant at some horizons but body fossils are rare. The sands were deposited in an overall estuarine situation, the small-scale cross-bedded units as migrating sand shoals in shallow water and

Gault

the large-scale cross-bedded horizons in subtidal channels (Wach & Ruffell, 1991). The trace fossil assemblages in the sands indicate that deposition occurred in a high energy environment in which the rate of deposition or erosion changed rapidly and there was considerable reworking of the sediment.

In Chale Bay, the southernmost Sandrock exposure, there are four coarsening-upward units; at Compton Bay only three such units are completely represented, the uppermost being reduced to a mere remnant; at Luccombe only three such units are present; and finally in the most northerly section at Red Cliff only two cycles remain. The evidence indicates that deposition of the Sandrock was followed by a regression and that, before the Carstone transgression took place, there was some local faulting and differential erosion.

The **Carstone Formation** comprises ferruginous, medium- to coarse-grained sands and sandstones with occasional thin conglomeratic horizons. The formation thickens from about 2 m at Compton Bay in the west to 22 m at Red Cliff in the east. The basal pebbly sands rest on an irregular erosion surface. This is an angular unconformity, although it is difficult to determine in individual sections. This unconformity marks a phase of regression, faulting and erosion that occurred prior to the Carstone transgression and the renewal of basin subsidence. Significantly, the Carstone is the earliest Cretaceous unit to be preserved north of the Isle of Wight Monocline, where it rests unconformably on Upper Jurassic rocks (Wach & Ruffell, 1991). The Carstone succession broadly becomes finer upwards but superimposed on this general trend are a number of minor fining-upward units. Bioturbation is abundant at some levels but body fossils are rare. While traditionally the Carstone has been included within the Lower Greensand Group, palaeontologically its affinities are with the overlying Gault. It has a gradational contact with, and clearly represents the basal transgressive unit of, the latter.

Gault Clay and Upper Greensand

In common with other areas in southern England, the Gault Clay and Upper Greensand form an unbroken sequence. The island lies midway between the clay dominated successions of southeast Kent and the sand and sandstone sequences of Dorset and southeast Devon. The two formations are thus approximately equal in development on the island.

The **Gault Clay** is a rather monotonous sequence of dark blue-grey silty muds. The base is usually transitional from the underlying Carstone and the boundary is arbitrarily fixed at the top of the uppermost brown sandstone in the succession. The upper boundary is also gradational but may be fixed conveniently at the base of the first buff silt or fine-grained sand in the sequence. The maximum thickness of the unit is about 30 m. At the eastern end of the

Gault

island the succession comprises alternations of silt/fine sand and clay-rich units but is generally sandy throughout in the south and west (Gale *et al.,* 1996). The only other obvious variations in lithology are sporadic glauconitic horizons and thin, pale brown phosphate-rich seams. Trace fossils, especially *Chondrites,* are common at some horizons. In many areas, the Gault Clay is involved in various forms of mass movement, especially along the southern coast. This has earned it the local name of the "Blue Slipper", although this term is often used on the island for any incompetent blue, green or grey mudrock regardless of stratigraphic position.

There has been no recent sedimentological research on the local Gault Clay but internal evidence supports the conclusion that it was produced by slow sedimentation in a shallow (about 100-200 m) marine environment. The dark grey colour, combined with the lack of abundant pyrite concretions, indicates that this is the restricted mud facies (Morris, 1979) in which the aerobic/anaerobic boundary was approximately at the sediment/water interface. There are no signs of either current transport or wave reworking, indicating that deposition took place in a quiet environment below wave base. Evidently, sedimentation occasionally ceased altogether and this allowed the development of phosphatic horizons. The clay mineralogy indicates that reworked Kimmeridge Clay and Oxford Clay were the source of the sediments and that there was a progressive rise in sea-level with time (Gale *et al.,* 1996).

The Gault Clay passes up transitionally into the **Upper Greensand.** The latter is essentially a glauconitic siltstone or fine-grained sand and sandstone with bands of calcareous and siliceous concretions. The boundary with the Gault Clay is placed at the base of the first buff silt or fine-grained sand in the succession. The upper boundary is everywhere marked by a change from the pale, slightly glauconitic silts of the Upper Greensand to the very dark green, richly glauconitic calcareous sandstone which forms the base of the overlying Chalk Group. The precise contact is often rather diffuse due to a combination of intense burrowing and erosion of the uppermost part of the Upper Greensand. The maximum thickness of the formation is 45 m.

The lowest part of the Upper Greensand (the "Passage Beds") consists of alternations of grey and buff silts and micaceous sandy muds and fine-grained muddy sands. The buff bands become thicker and more dominant upwards. The middle part of the formation (the "Malm Rock") comprises grey or buff glauconitic fine-grained sands and sandstones with irregular bands of large calcareous concretions and small phosphatic nodules. The uppermost part of the formation (the "Chert Beds") is the most conspicuous part of the succession. It consists of grey and buff glauconitic siltstones and fine-grained sandstones with bands of grey siliceous and calcareous concretions.

Chalk

There has been little recent work on the sedimentology of the Upper Greensand. The formation, together with the underlying Gault Clay, forms a coarsening-upward sequence which may represent a prograding shoreline with passage upwards from mud-dominated shelf deposits into shoreface sands. Most of the sequence is made up of thin rhythmic units consisting of a laminated lower part and an intensely bioturbated upper division. It is possible that these units were formed within the offshore shelf, offshore-shoreface transition and lower shoreface zones of a wave-dominated shoreline. Deposition in modern wave-dominated shorelines consists of alternations of storm-generated parallel-laminated silts and fine-grained sands and intensely bioturbated silty sands (e.g. Clifton *et al.,* 1971; Reineck & Singh, 1980; Howard *et al.,* 1972; Howard & Reineck, 1981). The occurrence of small brown phosphatic concretions and phosphatic replacements of fossil fragments at various horizons suggests that occasionally there were reduced sedimentation rates.

The origin of the chert in the Upper Greensand remains unresolved. The source of the silica was probably siliceous sponges whose spicules (or moulds of them) are abundant at some horizons. Since sedimentary laminations are deformed around chert concretions, silicification must have occurred prior to compaction and was therefore an early diagenetic process. The restriction of chert formation to certain beds suggests either that there were lithological controls on the movement and deposition of silica or alternatively that the silica source was not generally distributed.

Chalk Group

The Chalk Group comprises a very thick sequence of grey to white limestones and is one of the most widespread and distinctive geological units within the British stratigraphical succession. Virtually identical Cretaceous deposits, even containing the same fossils, occur across northern Europe and into western Asia as far east as Kazakhstan, on the eastern shores of the Caspian Sea, and also as far afield as Texas and Western Australia. In modern oceans, chalks form mostly in the deep-sea from accumulation of calcareous plankton - the calcite skeletons of myriad single-celled organisms which continually rain down from the surface. In the late Cretaceous, sea-levels rose to such an extent that pelagic chalk deposition took place on the continental shelf of northern Europe. Widespread chalk deposition continued for about 35 million years, until the end of the Cretaceous, and hundreds of metres of chalk were laid down over vast areas. Exactly how deep the late Cretaceous sea was in the British area is hard to determine, but maximum values of 300 m above present day sea-level are likely. At its greatest extent, the sea probably covered all of the British Isles, except the Scottish Highlands. The Cretaceous world differed significantly from our own in the apparent absence of polar ice-caps, warm temperate vegetation extending to

Chalk

85° north. Oxygen isotope analysis of Isle of Wight chalks indicates sea-surface temperatures in the range 20-30°C - pleasantly warmer than today.

Chalk is composed mainly of the skeletal remains of minute planktonic algae called Coccolithophoraceae. When these organisms die and decompose, their calcium carbonate skeletons disintegrate into separate rings called coccoliths, which are 5-10 microns in diameter. Coccoliths themselves break up into tiny (micron-sized) calcite plates. Technically, chalk is a friable to well-cemented biomicrite composed mainly of coccolithophorid debris. Coccoliths probably reached the sea-bed as the faecal pellets of copepods, small crustaceans forming part of the zooplankton. While coarser carbonate debris is present in all chalks, in some beds the finer fraction was winnowed away by sea floor currents to leave calcarenites or "shelly chalks". These consist of shells of single-celled foraminiferids, globular calcispheres, minute prismatic fragments of bivalve shells (especially the mussel-like *Inoceramus*), echinoderm debris and bryozoa.

The white limestones within the Chalk Group are often remarkably pure, containing between 90% and 98% calcium carbonate. Only in the lower part of the group does non-carbonate clastic debris become an important component. Some horizons contain up to 20% of clay minerals, together with a small amounts of silt and sand grade quartz, and the green mineral glauconite.

The Chalk Group sea floor was extensively burrowed by many organisms, including crustaceans. Consequently no small-scale primary sedimentary structures are preserved.

One of the most conspicuous features of any chalk cliff is the regular repetition of beds on the scale of a metre or less. In the Lower Chalk Formation, the alternations are of more or less marly chalk and the harder, more calcareous units which weather proud in exposures. In the lower part of the White Chalk Formation above, the alternations consist of nodular chalk and recessing thin wispy marls. In the succeeding flinty chalks, beds of flint nodules or sheets of black flint occur with striking regularity about every metre. Calculations indicate that the periodicity of all these rhythms is of the order of 20 to 40 thousand years. These values fall within the calculated periodicity of Milankovitch climatic cycles, which are caused by variations in the Earth's orbit altering the amount of solar radiation reaching the planet. The major Milankovitch frequencies are at 21, 40 and 100 thousand years. The Chalk rhythms are therefore seen as a record of late Cretaceous Milankovitch cycles, although the exact mechanism by which climatic change led to the formation of more or less marly beds or controlled flint formation remain unknown.

Chalk

Nodules and tabular sheets of black chert, commonly surrounded by a white patina, are abundant and conspicuous through much of the White Chalk. Nodular flints are concentrated in discrete, laterally continuous beds which occur rhythmically every metre or so through the sequence. Tabular flints, usually laterally discontinuous, occur both parallel to bedding and infilling fractures at an angle to the bedding. Flints pose numerous questions to even the casual observer. For example, why do they assume such odd and complex shapes? How did they form? Why do they occur in rhythmic beds? Folklore has provides many colourful answers to these questions, but geologists have only recently been able to provide scientific explanations.

Flints are of complex shape because they replace, and commonly overgrow, burrow infills. One of the commonest burrows in the Chalk Group is *Thalassinoides,* which consists of horizontal polygonal burrow networks joined by vertical tubes, all 1-10 cm in diameter. Flints commonly replace part of this network and consequently have elongated or branching forms. The surface of flints may clearly show the burrowed fabric of the infill it has replaced.

Flints are concretions that have grown within the sediment after its deposition, silica replacing calcite at specific sites. The necessary silica was derived from siliceous sponge spicules and probably also from diatoms and radiolarians, planktonic micro-organisms which have a silica skeleton. Silica secreted by these organisms, called opal-CT, was readily soluble in the sediment of the chalk sea floor. It then migrated downwards a few metres to the lower limit of occurrence of aerobic bacteria. It was precipitated in burrows, the requisite microchemical environment being produced by small concentrations of decaying organic matter. When first deposited, the silica was in the form of loose aggregates of tiny spheres of the mineral cristobalite. Subsequent increasing depth of burial led to the recrystallisation of the cristobalite into microcrystalline quartz nodules and sheets, that is the flint with its characteristic conchoidal fracture.

Flint concretions formed in bands parallel to successive positions of the sea-floor, even faithfully following small erosional channels and slumps which cut into the chalk sea bed. The positions of flint nodule beds were probably determined by frequent short breaks in deposition which allowed sufficient time for the silica to precipitate at the oxic-anoxic boundary. These breaks are now mostly invisible in homogeneous white chalk, although they are clear in the marlier lower parts of the Chalk Group succession.
The reduction or cessation of chalk sedimentation resulted in a break in deposition. Short breaks are marked by burrowed surfaces, highlighted by a slight contrast in colour between the sediment above and below the break. More prolonged non-deposition resulted in the development of hard nodules of chalk

beneath the sediment surface. These progressively expanded and coalesced to form a massively lithified chalk. Current scour commonly exposed this hard chalk as a rocky pavement on the sea bed called a hardground. Such exposed hardgrounds provided a suitable substrate for encrusting animals, such as oysters, and for numerous boring organisms. Nodular chalks and hardgrounds are commonly associated with the iron mineral pyrite, which changes on exposure to the yellow, orange and brown hues of various iron oxides. Hardgrounds may also have a coating of green glauconite and brown phosphate.

Within the White Chalk Formation, there are thin beds, 5 to 15 cm thick, of grey marl, which are conspicuous in some sections (e.g. upper part of Culver Cliff, Itinerary 2). While many were deposited as clay, some can be shown by geochemical analysis to have originated as volcanic ash which degraded to clay minerals after deposition. Whatever their origin, individual marl beds are traceable across southern England and are very useful for correlation.

For much of this century, the Chalk Group succession was subdivided into assemblage zones (rock units characterised by a distinctive association of fossils), following the authoritative work of Rowe, whose major paper on the Isle of Wight sequence was published in 1908 (see Gale & Cleevely, 1989). In the last twenty years, research has shown that widely traceable marker beds, including the hardgrounds, marls and flint bands, provide an excellent and very precise means of correlation over hundreds of kilometres within the Chalk Group of southern England. In addition, thicker lithological packages (members) can be defined and traced along the Chalk Group outcrop. The nomenclature used for these members is still in a state of flux, since researchers working in different regions have established separate local schemes. The nomenclature used throughout this guide is given in Table 2. The Chalk Group in the Isle of Wight is divided into two formations: the Lower Chalk and the White Chalk.

The **Lower Chalk Formation** is characterised by its higher clay content, grey appearance and conspicuous rhythmic bedding. It is divided into four members: Glauconitic Marl, Chalk Marl, Grey Chalk and Plenus Marls. **The Glauconitic Marl** at the base of the formation rests on a bored and slightly eroded surface of the Upper Greensand. This thin unit consists of glauconitic calcareous sand and silt with reworked cobbles of Upper Greensand at its base. It is extensively bioturbated (burrowed) throughout. Phosphatised and glauconitised calcareous pebbles are common as are phosphatised fossils and fossil fragments, especially sponges and ammonites. The basal part of the Glauconitic Marl varies in character laterally across the island (Figure 3). **The Chalk Marl,** which forms the bulk of the Lower Chalk sequence, consists of numerous grey marl/white limestone rhythmic couplets. Each couplet comprises a marl which grades upwards into a hard limestone. The top of the limestone is usually burrowed, the

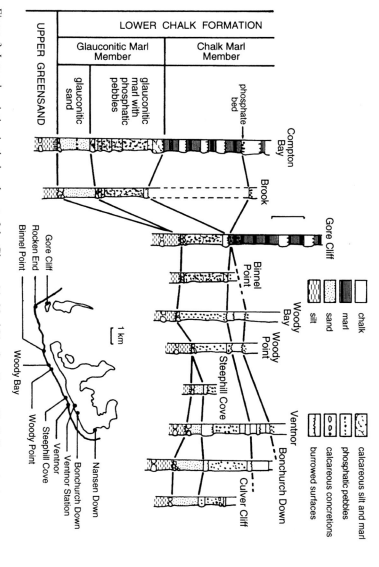

Figure 3. Lateral variation in the basal part of the Glauconitic Marl Member (Lower Chalk Formation) across the Isle of Wight (after Kennedy, 1969).

burrows being infilled with marl from the base of the overlying couplet and may present a conglomeratic or nodular appearance. The succeeding **Grey Chalk** also exhibits rhythmic bedding but contains appreciably less clay than the Chalk Marl and hence is lighter in colour. The top of the Lower Chalk is formed by the **Plenus Marls,** a predominantly grey marl unit with only thin pale soft limestones.

The base of the **White Chalk Formation** is marked by a sharp fall in clay content and thus consists essentially of white pure limestones with thin marl seams. The unit is subdivided into a number of members on the presence or absence of marls, the occurrence of nodular chalk and the style of bedding. The recognition of many of these members is difficult without experience. The **Ranscombe Member,** at the base of the formation, is conspicuously rhythmic and includes many thin marl beds. The **St. Margaret's Member** is strongly nodular, contains hardgrounds and several discrete thin marl beds. The **Broadstairs Member** comprises soft white chalk without marl seams but with numerous flint nodule beds. The **Newhaven Member** contains many thin marl seams and flint nodule bands. The **Culver Member** is a soft white chalk containing many nodular and tabular flint beds. The **Portsdown Member** comprises chalks with numerous thin marl partings and frequent flint bands. The highest chalk, present only at the western end of the island, is the **Studland Member,** a white chalk without marl seams but with numerous beds of flint nodules.

The unconformity between the Chalk and the overlying Palaeogene represents a gap of about 15 million years. After deposition of the younger Maastrichtian Chalk, which is present on the floor of the English Channel to the southwest of the island, uplift of the area during the earliest Palaeocene (Danian) resulted in a very gentle regional dip to the southwest. Subsequent peneplanation by marine erosion took place and the overlying Reading Clay oversteps progressively younger Chalk to the west. Thus, some 25 m of Chalk missing at Culver in the east of the island are present at Alum Bay in the west.

PALAEOGENE

Introduction

A total thickness of about 650 m of Palaeogene sediments is preserved in the northern part of the island. They rest unconformably on the Chalk Group. Immediately to the north of the Chalk Group outcrop, the Palaeogene strata are vertical or dip steeply northwards. Further north, such steep dips are replaced by flat-lying strata affected only by low amplitude folds (Figure 2). Altogether, the succession represents a period of some 20 million years, from late Palaeocene to earliest Oligocene.

Palaeogene

Throughout the Palaeogene, the British area lay on the western margins of the marine Northwest European Palaeogene Basin. Land existed essentially to the north and west. To the east, the Basin extended into the North Sea area, while to the south it was intermittently connected to the proto-Atlantic Ocean. The whole of the Isle of Wight Palaeogene succession is characterised by strata laid down during alternating advances (transgressions) and retreats (regressions) of the sea. Within this cyclic sequence, many environments are represented: shallow marine shelf to beaches, tidal flats, coastal marshes, lagoons, estuaries, rivers and lakes. There are also fossil soils which represent periods of exposure and weathering.

SERIES	DIVISION	GROUP	FORMATION	MEMBER	STAGE
Eocene	Late	Barton	Becton Sand		Marinesian
			Chama Sand		
			Barton Clay		
			Boscombe Sands		
	Middle	Bracklesham	Branksome Sand		Auversian
			Selsey Sand		
			Marsh Farm		Lutetian
			Poole / Earnley Sand		
			Poole / Wittering		Cuisian
	Early	Thames	London Clay	Whitecliff Sand	Ypresian
				Portsmouth Sand	
				London Clay Basement Bed	
Palaeocene	Late	Lambeth	Reading		Sparnacian

TABLE 3. Stratigraphy of the Early Palaeogene sequence on the Isle of Wight.

Palaeogene

SERIES	DIVISION	GROUP	FORMATION	MEMBER	STAGE
Oligocene	Early	Solent	Bouldnor	Cranmore	Rupelian
				Hamstead	
				Bembridge Marls	
Eocene	Late		Bembridge Limestone		Priabonian
			Headon Hill	Seagrove Bay	
				Osborne Marls	
				Fishbourne	
				Lacey's Farm Cliff End	
				Hatherwood Limestone	
				Linstone Chine	
				Colwell Bay	
				Totland Bay	

TABLE 4. Stratigraphy of the Late Palaeogene sequence on the Isle of Wight. The position of the Eocene/Oligocene boundary in the sequence remains uncertain, some workers considering that it lies at the base of the Bembridge Marls Member rather than the Hampstead Member as indicated here.

Much of the succession is dominated by muds (many sandy), although sands predominate at certain horizons and increase in importance westwards across the island. Non-clastic sediments are less common. Lignites and lignitic muds occur at intervals, whilst in the upper part of the succession there are a number of essentially freshwater limestones. The sequence has a prolific fossil biota. Gastropods and bivalves are the most common macro-invertebrate fossils. Microfossils include foraminiferids, including large forms such as *Nummulites* and *Alveolina,* and ostracods. Plant fossils occur at a number of horizons, whilst vertebrate remains have been most commonly found towards the top of the succession.

The Palaeogene succession in the Isle of Wight has been assigned to fourteen formations (Tables 3 & 4). The stratigraphic nomenclature used is after Edwards & Freshney (1987), except for the Solent Group, which includes the three youngest units, where that proposed by Insole & Daley (1985) is used. Almost the whole of the sequence may be examined in Whitecliff Bay (Itinerary 2). Strata of similar age, but of significantly different character, can be seen at Alum Bay (Itinerary 15) and in the contiguous Headon Hill section (Itinerary 16). The other Palaeogene itineraries (17, 18 and 19)) expose sequences within the Solent Group.

Palaeogene

Reading Formation

The unconformity with the Chalk Group is somewhat irregular, although no angular discordance is apparent. Immediately above the unconformity, a thin conglomerate and the succeeding sand represent the marine **Reading Formation Bottom Bed.** This basal unit is overlain by a sequence comprising mainly red and purple colour-mottled muds, which are considered to represent non-marine sediments subsequently subjected to weathering and soil formation.

London Clay

The London Clay is by no means as lithologically uniform as its name suggests. It comprises a series of coarsening-upward units (see King, 1981). Each unit has a sharp base, sometimes marked by pebbles, representing a transgressive event. Above the base come mainly silty muds containing marine fossils and usually glauconite, reflecting a gradual increase in the depth of water. The upper part of the units are characterised by two lithologies, both of which reflect shallowing associated with periods of regression. One lithology is heterolithic, consisting of laminated silty sands and muds which are interpreted as tidal flat deposits. The other comprises well-sorted, cross-bedded sands which are considered to have been deposited in tidal channels. These sands were formerly called the "Bagshot Sands" but are now assigned to two members within the London Clay: the **Portsmouth Sand** and the overlying **Whitecliff Sand.**

Bracklesham Group

The Bracklesham Group is a complex unit showing considerable vertical and lateral variation. Like the London Clay, it comprises a rhythmic sequence. The marine character of the lower part of each unit is well seen in Whitecliff Bay (Itinerary 2), where glauconitic sands and sandy muds contain marine molluscs and *Nummulites*. Plint (1983) suggested that such sediments were deposited under sediment-starved offshore shelf conditions, the occasional bands of shells representing storm-generated lag deposits. The upper parts of the units consist of heterolithic sediments including not only interbedded muds, silts and sands but also lignites. These were formed during regressive phases in shallower waters, occasionally becoming intertidal and in extreme cases vegetated brackish lagoons.

At the western end of the island, the character of the Bracklesham Group is somewhat different. In Alum Bay (Itinerary 15) it is virtually devoid of marine macro-invertebrate fossils and glauconitic sediments are uncommon. The succession in this area represents more marginally marine conditions than in Whitecliff Bay. Here, the lower parts of each unit comprise sands within which Plint (1983) recognised a mixture of beach, fluvial and aeolian dune deposits. The upper parts of the units are heterolithic, interbedded muds, silts and sands interpreted as tidal lagoon and tidal channel deposits. The repeated occurrence of lignites and palaeosols (fossil soils) within the heterolithic sequences probably represents coastal marshes.

Palaeogene

The complex internal variation within the Bracklesham Group sequence makes sub-division difficult. Currently six formations are recognised (Table 4). Four of these are represented in Whitecliff Bay: **Wittering, Earnley Sand, Marsh Farm** and **Selsey Sand Formations** in ascending order. In Alum Bay, the Earnley and Selsey Sand Formations are absent, the **Poole Formation** interdigitates with the Wittering Formation in the lower part of the succession, and the **Branksome Sand Formation** forms the top of the group.

Barton Group

The Barton Group comprises four formations: **Boscombe Sand, Barton Clay, Chama Sand** and **Becton Sand** (formerly Barton Sand) in ascending order. On the Isle of Wight, the Boscombe Sand Formation is only exposed in Alum Bay. It comprises well-sorted sands thought to have been deposited in a beach or shoreface environment. The succeeding Barton Clay consists of more or less silty muds with a diverse marine molluscan fauna, with *Nummulites* at some horizons. The occurrence of bands rich in glauconite suggests that it represents sediment-starved offshore shelf conditions. The thin sandy muds of the Chama Sand probably reflect poor sorting below wave base in a lower shoreface environment. At the top of the group come the mainly clean quartz sands of the Becton Sand Formation. These sands are devoid of body fossils, although burrows occur. This unit represents middle/upper shoreface to beach conditions.

Solent Group

The Solent Group comprises two predominantly clastic formations, the lower **Headon Hill Formation** and the upper **Bouldnor Formation,** separated by a primarily carbonate unit, the **Bembridge Limestone.** Both clastic units are subdivided into members (Table 4).

This part of the Palaeogene sequence was first described by Forbes (1853) who termed it the 'Fluvio-marine Tertiaries'. Whilst this term is no longer used, it reflects the early recognition that the youngest parts of the island succession were deposited mainly in non-marine environments. In fact, fully marine conditions are only represented at two horizons, the Brockenhurst Bed at the base of the Colwell Bay Member and perhaps in the Corbula Beds at the top of the Cranmore Member.

Studies of the fossil assemblages present, particularly the molluscs and ostracods, have shown that the Solent Group was laid down in conditions ranging from almost marine through brackish to freshwater, the latter being particularly well represented by the Bembridge Limestone and the limestones within the Headon Hill Formation (Paul, 1989; Armenteros *et al.,* 1997). Deposition evidently took place in an extensive complex low-lying paralic (marginal marine) environment. In such an area, salinities would have varied from place to place and through time depending on the complex interplay of a number of factors, including subsidence, global sea-level changes, proximity to river channels and climate.

The Solent Group sediments are rich in fossils, especially gastropods and bivalves. The famous Insect Limestone, a fine-grained calcareous mudstone near the base of the Bembridge Marls member, has yielded a large insect fauna, especially in Thorness Bay (Itinerary 19). A varied vertebrate fauna, including fish, amphibians, reptiles, birds and mammals, has been recovered from a number of horizons within the group. Plant remains, including fruits, seeds and leaves, occur at various levels but are particularly abundant in the Bembridge Marls Member at Hamstead (Itinerary 18).

In the absence of an agreed international standard, the position of the Eocene/Oligocene boundary has been the subject of discussion for many years. Micropalaeontological studies (Liengjarern *et al.,* 1980) suggest that, on the Isle of Wight, it may be placed either at the bottom of the Bembridge Marls Member or at at the level of the Black Band, the base of the Hamstead Member.

?NEOGENE AND QUATERNARY

After the deposition of the Bouldnor Formation, there was a long period of uplift and erosion. Folding on the Isle of Wight Monocline, which had probably commenced in the Eocene, reached its culmination in the Miocene and formed the existing structural grain of the region. The area then underwent erosion to form the landscape as we see it today. This final phase of the geological history of the island is very poorly known. The only available evidence comprises relatively thin, disconnected patches of unconsolidated sediments. Few of these Drift or Superficial deposits can be dated, making their correlation and interpretation largely speculative. Table 5 provides the currently perceived relative chronology of the ?Neogene and Quaternary deposits.

Thin, unbedded deposits of angular flint pebbles in a muddy sand matrix occur in isolated patches at high levels on the Chalk downs of St. Boniface and Bowcombe. These have been termed the **Angular Flint Gravels of the Downs** and are a local variant of the Clay-with-Flints found elsewhere in southern England. Such deposits are are considered to be a residual deposits formed by *in situ* dissolution of the White Chalk Formation possibly with the addition of clay washed down from an overlying veneer of Palaeogene sediments (Loveday, 1960). The age of these deposits is uncertain but they are generally believed to have been formed over a long period of time during the Neogene to early Pleistocene.

Neogene and Quaternary

SERIES	STAGE	STRATIGRAPHIC UNITS
Holocene	Flandrian	Alluvium
Pleistocene	Devensian	Head Brickearth
	Ipswichian	Bembridge Raised Beach Newtown Complex (*pars*) River Terrace Gravels (*pars*)
	Wolstonian	
	Hoxnian	Steyne Wood Clay River Terrace Gravels (*pars*)
	Anglian	?↑ Plateau Gravels
	pre-Anglian	?↑ Angular Flint Gravels of the Downs (= Clay-with Flints)
Pliocene		

TABLE 5. Possible stratigraphic relationships of the Quaternary deposits of the isle.

During the late Pliocene and Pleistocene, southern Britain experienced numerous climatic changes. At one end of the spectrum of variation, ice sheets spread southwards across the British Isles and, while they never reached this far south, they nonetheless imposed cold periglacial conditions here. At other times the climate was warm temperate. The chronology of these changes remains elusive. The most widely used chronostratigraphic scheme covering these changes was produced by the Geological Society's sub-committee on the Quaternary (Mitchell *et al.*, 1973; see Table 5), which was based on palynological data. However, oxygen isotope data derived from deep sea cores indicates that there were 32 glacial/interglacial cycles during the Pleistocene (Shackleton *et al.*, 1991), many more than can be accommodated in the Geological Society's system. It has therefore become the practice to utilise both the latter and oxygen isotope (δ^{18}O) stages where possible, while recognising that correlation between the two remains imprecise.

Reconstructions of the palaeodrainage of the Hampshire Basin suggests that by the mid-Pleistocene, if not earlier, the region was drained by a large easterly-flowing river and its tributaries, the Solent River (e.g. Reid, 1902; Dyer, 1975; West, 1980). While the details remain uncertain, it is clear that the palaeogeographic development of this drainage system was complex, with

Neogene and Quaternary

neotectonic, erosional and depositional processes acting against a background of the repeated glacial/interglacial cycles.

When sea-level was very low, during the cold stages, the Solent River and its tributaries flowed through a system of gravel-floored channels as much as 46 m below current sea-level (Everard, 1954; Dyer, 1975) (Figure 4a). The prevailing periglacial climate during the last glacial (Devensian) resulted in the development locally of **Head** and **Brickearth.** The former are deposits produced

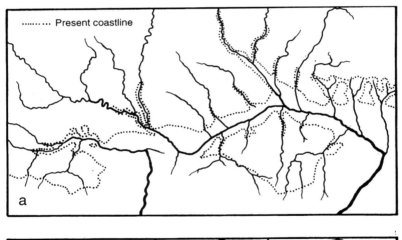

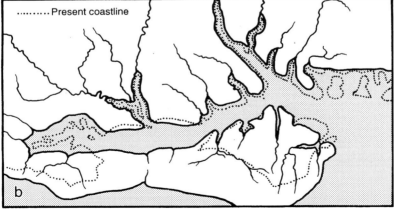

Figure 4. a. Schematic geography of the Solent area during Pleistocene glacial periods (after Everard, 1954).

b. Schematic geography of the Solent area during the Ipswichian interglacial.

Neogene and Quaternary

by downslope movement of weathered bedrock and drift by a mixture of solifluction and downwash, while the latter appears to represent either primary or reworked loess.

During the interglacials, sea-level was probably as high as or higher than it is today and the lower reaches of the river system were submerged to form broad estuaries (Figure 4b). Several different types of deposit were formed locally during the interglacials. The **Steyne Wood Clay** (Holyoak & Preece, 1983; Preece & Scourse, 1987; Preece *et al.*, 1990) and the **Newtown Complex** (Munt & Burke, 1987) represent intertidal mudflats, the former deposited during the Hoxnian ($\delta^{18}O$ stage 11), while latter was laid down in the Ipswichian ($\delta^{18}O$ stage stage 5e). The **Bembridge Raised Beach** (Preece & Scourse, 1987; Preece *et al.*, 1990) formed as a barrier beach during the Ipswichian ($\delta^{18}O$ stage 5e). The most difficult deposits to place chronologically are the **Older River Gravels** (formerly Plateau Gravels) and the **River Terrace Deposits.** These were laid down as valley fills. Although Everard (1954) and others have interpreted these deposits to be partly marine in origin, their character (lithology, sedimentary structures, planar upper surfaces, apparent slight seaward gradient) suggest that they are fluvial deposits (Edwards & Freshney, 1987).
At the end of the Pleistocene, sea-level began to rise and began to submerge the lowest parts of the local Solent River system. As this transgression took place, muds and peats accumulated in the newly formed estuaries, sedimentation usually keeping pace with the rising sea-level (Hodson & West, 1972). Initially, sea-level rose rapidly (West, 1972) and several coastal Mesolithic occupation sites, such as those in the Medina Valley, were submerged (Basford, 1980). The Solent River drainage pattern was finally disrupted when the Chalk ridge between the island and the Isle of Purbeck was breached by fluvial and/or marine processes, probably in late Devensian or early Flandrian times (Devoy, 1987; Nicholls, 1987).

Since its separation from the mainland, the island's coastline has retreated to its present position due in part to submergence of low-lying areas. However, coastal erosion has also been important factor. Of the current coastline of about 97 km, about 18 km comprises steep rock cliffs subject mainly to rock falls, topples and slides and some 42 km consists of mud-rich rock sequences affected to a greater or lesser extent by landslides (Hutchinson, 1965). Most of the main types of coastal mass movement can be seen on the island. They are particularly well seen in the area known as the Undercliff (Itinerary 8). There is no standard classification of mass movements, but that produced by Hutchinson (1984) (Figure 5) is used in throughout this guide.

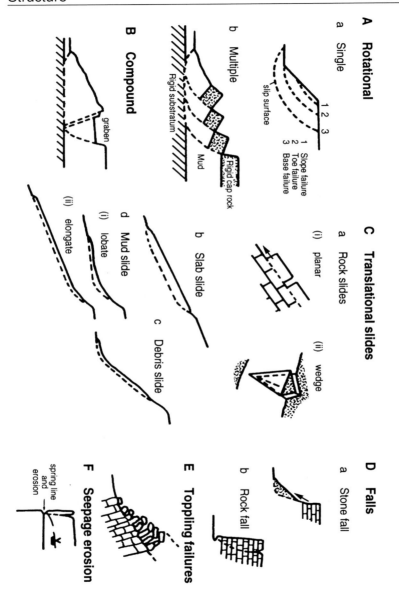

Figure 5. Classification of mass movements on the Isle of Wight (modified from Hutchinson, 1984).

Structure

a **End Triassic**

b **End Wealden**

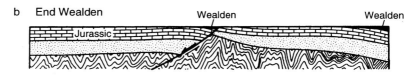

c **End Cretaceous**

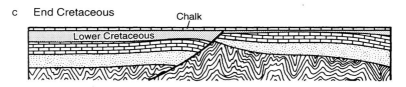

d **Mid-Palaeogene**

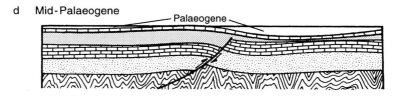

e **English Channel**

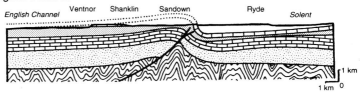

Figure 6. Schematic tectonic evolution of the Isle of Wight area from the Triassic.

STRUCTURE

The structural geology of the Island is dominated by the *en echelon* asymmetrical Brighstone and Sandown Anticlines which parallel a northward-facing E-W monoclinal flexure lying a short distance to the north (Figure 2). Similar structural features occur in south Dorset to the west, and it has become

Structure

the convention to refer this group of folds as the Purbeck-Wight Monocline. On the island, the monoclinal flexure consists of two arcuate segments which are concave to the south, suggesting that they represent the expression of deep-seated faults which are considered to be related to Variscan thrusts in the basement (Stoneley, 1982; Chadwick *et al.,* 1983). The Palaeogene strata north of the monoclinal flexure exhibit a few very low-amplitude folds which trend NW-SE. In the last three decades, as a result of hydrocarbon exploration, the subsurface stratigraphy and structure of the Wessex-Channel Basin has become known and its tectonic evolution has been unravelled (Figure 6).

Geophysical studies within the basin (Whittaker & Chadwick, 1984; Whittaker, 1986; Whittaker, *et al.,* 1986; BIRPS & ECORS, 1986) show that the crust possesses three layers. The composition of the lowest layer (15 to 33 km deep) is uncertain but it is believed to comprise the crystalline basement rocks. The middle layer (2 to 15 km deep) comprises Precambrian and late Palaeozoic rocks and its upper surface marks the top of the Variscan basement. The geology of the Variscan basement has been mapped and the available data indicate that beneath the Isle of Wight it comprises only deformed Devonian rocks (Smith, 1986; Sellwood & Scott, 1986; Lake & Karner, 1987). The upper part of the Variscan basement is crossed by numerous E-W trending, southward dipping structures which are probably Variscan thrust zones, that beneath the Isle of Wight being the Purbeck-Wight Thrust Zone. The uppermost crustal layer consists of the relatively undeformed Permian, Mesozoic and Palaeogene cover sequence.

From the late Carboniferous onwards, the crust within the basin began to undergo N-S extension. The Variscan thrusts were reactivated as normal faults with south-directed downthrows and extension on these faults controlled basin subsidence (Penn, 1985; Chadwick, 1985a, 1986). There is little evidence of faulting in the eastern parts of the basin until the very late Triassic (Chadwick, 1986). Movements continued intermittently until the early Cretaceous. The faulting caused the formation of a number of E-W oriented asymmetric grabens and half-grabens. In the present context, a Channel Basin to the south was separated from the Weald and Pewsey Basins by the Hampshire-Dieppe High. The pre-Upper Cretaceous Mesozoic succession abruptly thins over the Purbeck-Wight Fault, which marks the southern boundary of the Hampshire-Dieppe High, and gradually thins southwards onto the Central Channel High. This tectonic activity was probably related to spreading phases in the Atlantic and/or to events in the Tethys region to the south.

Fault movements in the early late Jurassic (late Oxfordian) coincided with a global fall in sea-level. In the Wessex-Channel Basin, the deposition of the non-marine Wealden Group marks the culmination of subsidence, sedimentation

Structure

taking place locally within the fault-bounded Channel Basin (Chadwick, 1985b, 1986). Accumulation of the Wealden Group in the Isle of Wight area may have been largely restricted to a relatively narrow E-W basin south of the Purbeck-Wight Fault scarp (Insole & Hutt, 1994). At the same time erosion took place on the various highs within the Wessex-Channel Basin, producing the so-called late Cimmerian (pre-Albian) erosion surface. Over 400 m of Upper Jurassic sediments are thought to have been removed from the crest of the local Hampshire-Dieppe High at this time (Chadwick, 1985b). Some of the erosional debris was evidently shed southwards into the Channel Basin, Upper Jurassic pebbles occurring in the Wealden and Lower Greensand Groups on the island (Garden, 1991; Radley, 1993). By the early Aptian, active crustal extension had ceased and regional, unfaulted subsidence was established (Chadwick, 1986). Rising global sea-level at this time is marked by the late Cimmerian unconformity produced by an Aptian and Albian transgression. Exposures on the southern coast of the island show the Carstone resting on an erosion surface at the top of the Sandrock, but subsurface data indicate that north of the Isle of Wight Monocline it rests on various mid-Jurassic units (Chadwick, 1985b, 1986). During mid-Cretaceous (post-Carstone) period, the area was stable. A global fall in sea-level occurred at the end of the Cretaceous resulting in exposure and erosion producing the pre-Palaeogene unconformity.

In the latest Cretaceous or early Palaeogene, N-S compression began in this area. Consequently, a reversal of the earlier movement occurred on the pre-existing E-W normal faults within the Wessex-Channel Basin (Falcon & Kent, 1960; Kenolty et al., 1981; Stoneley, 1982; Chadwick et al., 1983; Chadwick, 1985c, 1991; Penn, 1985). The extensional basin subsidence patterns were reversed, structural highs becoming sedimentary basins and structural lows were uplifted and underwent erosion. The Channel Basin was uplifted over 1000 m between the late Cretaceous and the Miocene (Chadwick, 1991). Such basin inversion, was a common feature in northern Europe from mid-Cretaceous onwards (e.g. Ziegler, 1981). The southern margin of the Palaeogene Hampshire-Dieppe Basin was defined at this time.

Exactly when compression and inversion began remains uncertain, but sedimentological evidence indicates intermittent syn-depositional movements were taking place in the late Lower to Upper Eocene (Plint, 1982; Murray & Wright, 1974) and the low-amplitude folds which affect the Palaeogene sediments to the north of the monoclinal flexure are believed to be of late Eocene to early Oligocene age (Daley & Edwards, 1971). However, the tectonic phase reached its culmination in the early Oligocene to early Miocene when N-S compressional stresses were generated by N-S convergence in the Alps. The Purbeck-Wight Monocline and the other narrow north-facing E-W flexure zones in the region assumed their present forms at this time.

Bembridge Foreland

There is growing evidence to suggest that tectonic deformation continued after the early Miocene. Bevan & Hancock (1986, 1987) record the presence of NW-SE trending vertical extension joints which are younger than the E-W flexures They considered that these resulted from regional tension produced by the late Neogene phase of NW-SE Alpine convergence. Furthermore, Preece *et al.* (1990) have discussed the tectonic implications of the occurrence of Middle Pleistocene (?Hoxnian) intertidal muds at about 40 m above sea-level at Bembridge and littoral sands at the same elevation and probably the same age in southern Hampshire and Sussex (e.g. Boxgrove). Recent research suggests that during the Middle and Late Pleistocene, sea-levels did not reach elevations of more than +10 m O.D. Preece *et al.* (1990) concluded that regional tectonic uplift took place in the eastern Hampshire Basin during or since the Middle Pleistocene. While it is possible that renewed movement on the basement faults took place locally, it seems more probable that a broader scale uplift which affected southeast England and the adjacent continent since the Pliocene was responsible (see Preece *et al.* 1990 for a detailed discussion).

ITINERARIES

1. Bembridge Foreland
The low cliffs around Bembridge Foreland provide discontinuous exposures of the Quaternary (Ipswichian and Devensian) deposits of the northeastern corner of the Island (Figure 7).

The area is accessible either from the car park at the Foreland (655873) or that adjacent to the Lifeboat Station, Lane End (656881), although neither is suitable for coaches. Parts of this itinerary are accessible at all states of the tide, but a medium or low tide is preferable. Total walking distance, including return, about 4 km.

References. Codrington (1870), Preece & Scourse (1987), Preece *et al.* (1990).

Descend to the beach from the Foreland car park and walk south into Howgate Bay. Below Foreland Fields (652873, locality 1.1), the cliffs show the grey-green clays of the Palaeogene Bouldnor Formation disappearing beneath the Quaternary gravels. From this point northwards, there are intermittent exposures of these gravels (Figure 7). The gravels rest on an eroded surface of the Bouldnor Formation. This erosion surface falls from about 18 m O.D. near Howgate to about high water mark at Ethel Point. The gravels also thin in the same direction, from more than 15 m below Foreland Fields to about 1 m in the north. At the southern end of the exposure, the deposit terminates abruptly against a palaeocliff cut in Bouldnor Formation muds. This palaeocliff appears to trend approximately east-west.

Bembridge Foreland

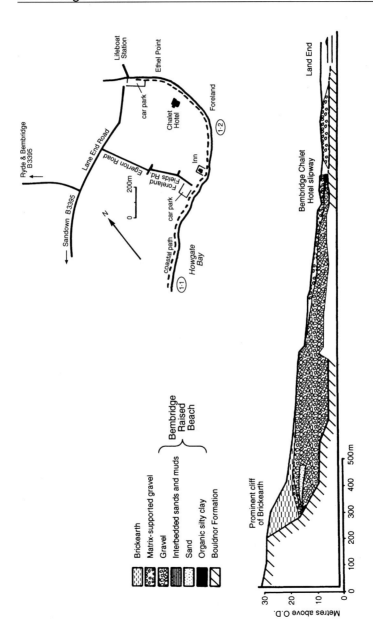

Figure 7. Location map and cliff profile from Bembridge School to Lane End, Bembridge (after Preece et al., 1990).

Bembridge Foreland

When examined in detail, the gravel deposit can be seen to comprise two units. The lower unit consists of a bedded, clast-supported, reddish-brown conglomerate with a maximum thickness of 12 m. The bedding dips gently (8° to 13°) north-east. The clasts are well-rounded and are mostly of flint, although some Cretaceous and Jurassic chert, ironstone, igneous and low grade metamorphic rocks are also present. This petrology would suggest that the deposit was derived from the southwest. The pebbles exhibit crescentic chattermarks, typically produced by percussion when stones are rolled together. While the bulk of the deposit is conglomeratic, some lenses of sand are usually visible, particularly towards the south western end of the section. This conglomerate is the **Bembridge Raised Beach** and is interpreted as a high-energy beach gravels laid down during a period of high relative sea-level in a coastal environment and probably represents a spit. A thermoluminescence date of about 115 thousand years (i.e. within the Ipswichian interglacial) has been obtained from a sandy lens within these gravels (Southgate *in* Preece *et al.*, 1990).

The upper unit comprises a white, matrix-supported, poorly bedded conglomerate which becomes muddier towards the north east. It has a maximum thickness of 3·5 m at the Bembridge Chalet Hotel slipway and is absent along much of the section (Figure 7). The matrix is a poorly sorted mixture of clay, silt and sand. The fabric varies both laterally and vertically with discrete sand bodies and concentrations of clasts, often termed "stone nests", and indistinct contorted bedding. In the upper part of the gravel, pebbles often have their long axes oriented vertically. These features are particularly well seen in the area around the Bembridge Chalet Hotel slipway, north of the Coastguard Station. Such features are known to be produced by repeated freezing and thawing of ground ice in periglacial areas where the mean annual temperature is about 0°C. The character of the white gravel suggest that it is a solifluction deposit, that is, formed by downslope movement of water-saturated material, in this case the underlying Bembridge Raised Beach gravel mixed with mud derived from the Bouldnor Formation. The upper unit is therefore considered to be of Devensian age.

These gravels are blanketed by what has been described as "brickearth". It comprises a well-sorted silt and, in places, contains clear evidence of bedding in the form of pebble stringers. It neither exhibits columnar jointing nor rootlet-derived pinhole voids characteristic of a *primary* loess (wind deposited silt), but may represent a loess reworked by colluvial processes (i.e. downslope creep and hillwash). This unit thickens southwestwards to a maximum of 10·5 m just before it terminates against the same palaeocliff as the Bembridge Raised Beach. This horizon has produced one Acheulian ovate implement *in situ* (Codrington, 1870) and two others have been found in situations which suggest that they came from the same horizon. It is considered that these artefacts became incorporated in the brickearth during its formation. **If further specimens are discovered, they**

Bembridge Foreland

should be reported to the Museum of Isle of Wight Geology, Sandown.
Thermoluminescence dates obtained from the brickearth range from 16 to 21·5
thousand years old (i.e. late Devensian)(Parkes & Rendell, 1988).

Continue further north to the Foreland (658876, locality 1.2). The low cliffs here
may provide further discontinuous Quaternary sections, but exposures are very
variable and sometimes very little may be visible, particularly since the
construction of coastal protection. At the base of the sequence are coarse sands
and gravels, the lateral equivalents to those seen in the south and part of the
Bembridge Raised Beach. These are overlain by and appear to grade laterally
into interbedded pale grey sands and blue-grey muds, the latter being more
frequent and thicker towards the base. These deposits have not yielded fossils
but, from their stratigraphic position, are believed to be intertidal beach deposits.
In some places, these coarse clastic sediments grade laterally into up to 1 m of
very dark grey-brown organic mud with scattered rounded black flint pebbles.
Neither macrofossils nor microfauna have been found. Pollen samples from this
level are dominated by the trees *Quercus* (oak) and *Carpinus* (hornbeam), the
shrub *Corylus* (hazel), and herbs such as Gramineae (grasses). The sediment and
its pollen spectrum suggests that deposition occurred in a low-energy coastal
environment, probably a saltmarsh, with a forested hinterland. The pollen data
also indicate that deposition of the organic clay began at the end of the early
temperate substage (zone IIb) and continued through the succeeding late
temperate substage (zone III) of the Ipswichian interglacial. The evidence
indicates that the Bembridge Raised Beach is a single upward-fining sequence
comprising the gravel, interbedded sands and muds and the organic mud.
Overlying the Ipswichian deposits is a matrix-supported gravel and a thin
brickearth, both the local equivalents of the soliflucted gravels and brickearth
seen to the south, and of Devensian age.

Further northwest, immediately southeast of Bembridge Lifeboat Station
(657881, locality 1.3), exposures behind the modern sea defences exhibit a
sequence of angular flint gravels and silty sands within which is a sedge-peat.
Insect fossils, plant macrofossils and pollen from the peat and the underlying
sand all indicate a non-marine environment. The stratigraphical relationship
between these sands and the Bembridge Raised Beach is uncertain because of
the lack of exposure in the intervening cliffs. The pollen data is insufficient for
dating but it is possible that this sequence was deposited towards the end of the
Ipswichian at the seaward end of a small palaeovalley.

**The starting point of the itinerary can be reached either by returning along
the foreshore or by exiting the beach at Lane End (656881) and following
the coastal path (BB10) back to the Foreland.**

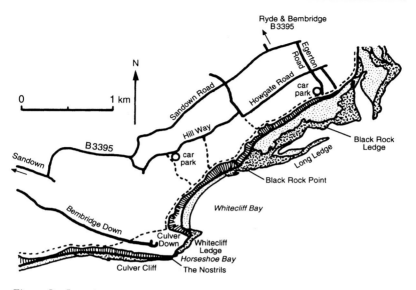

Figure 8a. Location map.

2. Whitecliff Bay

The cliffs forming the southern end of Whitecliff Bay and their southerly continuation in Culver Cliff (Itinerary 3) afford the most complete and reasonably accessible section through the entire Chalk Group succession in southern England. In Whitecliff Bay itself, within a distance of just over one kilometre, a little over 500 m of late Palaeocene to late Eocene strata are visible. These exposures provide the most continuous section of this age in northwest Europe and is consequently of international, as well as national, importance. The cyclic transgressive/regressive nature of the Palaeogene succession is clearly demonstrated by the variable character of lithology and fauna. Whitecliff Bay and Alum Bay/Headon Hill (see Itineraries 15 and 16) provide serial sections through the shallow marine and nonmarine sediments deposited during the Palaeogene. It is instructive to compare and contrast the successions exposed at these two sites.

There is no convenient public car park close to Whitecliff Bay, the nearest being at the Foreland (655873), although this is unsuitable for coaches. It may be possible to park small vehicles in the car park at the Whitecliff Bay Holiday Park (639865) outside the summer season. From either parking place, it is possible to reach the centre of Whitecliff Bay via public footpaths (Figure 8a).

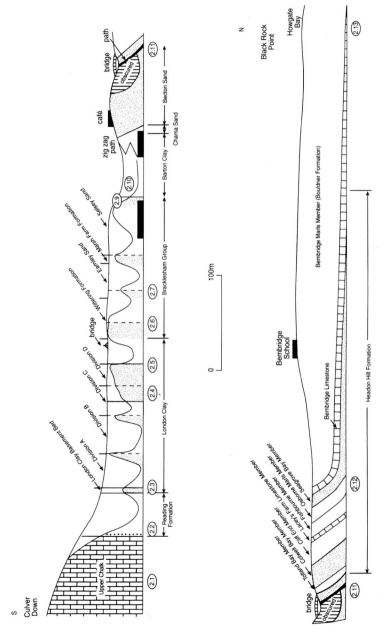

Figure 8b. Cliff profile from Horseshoe Bay to Howgate Bay, Bembridge.

Whitecliff Bay

Most of the section can be reached at any time except at high water spring tides. Total walking distance about 4 km, mostly over shingle beaches.

References. Armenteros *et al.* (1997), Daley (1973), Daley & Edwards (1974, 1990), Fisher (1862), Insole & Daley (1985), King (1981), Lord & Bown (1987), Plint (1983), Rowe (1908), White (1921).

Descend to the beach down the zigzag path and walk to the southern point of the bay. From here the general arrangement of the strata can be seen (Figure 8b). In the foreground, the vertical Chalk Group and lower Palaeogene succession represent the northern limb of the Sandown Anticline. Towards the northern end of the bay, the dip changes rapidly over a short distance such that at Black Rock (645865) a northerly dip of about 5° is apparent.

At low tide, it is possible to walk round the point to reach Whitecliff Ledge, the White Horse Ledge and even reach as far as the Nostrils (locality 2.1). The **White Chalk Formation** here dips at about 80°N. **This traverse should only be attempted on a falling tide and it is vital to return across Whitecliff Ledge three hours before high tide. It is therefore best to walk to the southernmost point of the itinerary and work back towards Whitecliff Bay. Great care is necessary on the slippery rocks. The section beyond White Horse Ledge is very dangerous and should only be attempted by experienced workers. The cliffs are vertical throughout and a hard hat should always be worn here. It is not advisable to work beneath the cliffs either after frost or heavy rain, when there is a constant rain of debris, sometimes quite large. This part of the itinerary should not be attempted during stormy weather.**

The Nostrils, two adjacent caves, are situated on the south of White Horse Ledge. They have been eroded into two marl seams, the East Cliff and Hope Point Marls. Horseshoe Bay (locality 2.1), north of White Horse Ledge, has a shingle beach and provides a spectacular but rather inaccessible section through the clean white chalks with numerous bands of irregular flint nodules and, less commonly, tabular sheets of the **Broadstairs Member.** Some of the flint bands are offset by small-scale faults by as much as 1 m. The base of the **Newhaven Member** is located on the northeastern side of the bay and is marked by the appearance of thin marl partings. The lower part of this member contains plates of the globular, long-armed stemless crinoid *Uintacrinus*. In the beds above this, the related and equally strange crinoid *Marsupites* occurs. Behind the fall at the northeastern corner of Horseshoe Bay, flints are absent over a 16 m interval and nodular chalks containing several hardgrounds are developed. This is the **Whitecliff Ledge Member,** a local development forming a lens within the Newhaven Member. Just 10 km to the west, at Downend Quarry near Arreton, this unit is represented by ordinary white chalks with flints and thin marls typical of the Newhaven Member. The hardground surfaces are coated with the blue-green mineral glauconite and contain silvery nodules of the iron sulphide mineral marcasite. Calcarenite (carbonate sand) developments may be seen above the hardgrounds. The upper part of the Newhaven Member above the Whitecliff Ledge Member comprises flinty chalks containing thin marls. It is succeeded by soft white chalks containing numerous beds of flint nodules and some tabular flint sheets, the **Culver Member.** About 30 m west of the point where Whitecliff Bay begins, a thin marl bed marks the base of the overlying **Portsdown Member.** From here to the top of the succession there are flinty chalks with thin marls. On the foreshore platform, the Portsdown Member is conspicuously rhythmic. The spherical sponge *Porosphaera,* the small echinoid *Echinocorys subconicula* and the belemnite *Belemnitella mucronata* can usually be found in this unit.

In the southern corner of Whitecliff Bay, the unconformity between the White Chalk Formation and the **Reading Formation** may be visible (locality 2.2). No angular discordance is apparent, but the top of the White Chalk Formation is potholed and irregular. A thin conglomerate, containing a mixture of angular and well rounded flints and grey pebbly sand rest on this surface (the **Reading Formation Bottom Bed**). The remainder of the Reading Formation comprises unfossiliferous, predominantly red colour-mottled muds which may be the result of contemporaneous soil development. Much of the sequence is obscured by slips and vegetation. Apart from silicified echinoids in the basal conglomerate and a few derived Chalk Group microfossils elsewhere, no fossils have so far been found in the Reading Formation.

The Reading Formation is overlain by the **London Clay** (about 142 m) which, following current usage, includes the distinctive yellow and whitish sands formerly called the "Bagshot Sands". At the base of the formation (locality 2.3) is the **London Clay Basement Bed** (2.8 m) (the Oldhaven Formation of King, 1981). The Reading Formation/London Clay contact is sharp and is overlain by a thin, patchily lithified, conglomeratic silty sand containing flint, Chalk and Reading Formation pebbles. This basal unit is overlain by glauconitic silty sands with thin muds and calcareous concretions. Shell-rich lenses contain abundant worm tubes (*Ditrupa*), marine molluscs and occasional sharks teeth.

The remainder of the London Clay comprises four transgressive-regressive cycles (the Divisions A, B, C and D of King, 1981), separated by erosion surfaces (often overlain by a pebble bed) representing major transgressive events. The cycles are essentially coarsening-upward in nature. Erosion of the softer muds forming the lower parts of the first three cycles has produced the gullies in the present cliff profile. **The muds at the base of Cycle 1 have been**

badly affected by slumping in recent years and may extend as an "apron" over part of the foreshore. As a result it is sometimes impossible to reach the southernmost part of the bay at high tide.

Cycle 1 (37.5 m) has a glauconitic, pebbly base. Above, clayey silts are succeeded by a fine sand containing *Ophiomorpha* burrows. The top of the cycle comprises bioturbated silts. Fossils are not abundant due to the decalcification, but *Glycymeris, Panopea, Ostrea* and *Streptolathyris* occur. **Cycle 2** (39.8 m) has a sharp base but pebbles occur rarely. The lower part of this cycle is poorly exposed but comprises silty clays with lines of septarian concretions. A glauconitic sand occurs about 8 m above the base of the cycle. Above this glauconitic horizon, *Arctica* and *Pecten* are common. The uppermost 16 m of the cycle comprises lenticular bedded and laminated sands and silts. Within this part of the succession, a relatively thick sand contains contemporaneously truncated water-escape structures.

The base of **Cycle 3** (31.6 m) is marked by a thin band of black flint pebbles, overlain by silty muds coarsening up into sandy silts. The bivalve *Pholadomya* often occurs in life position and, in association with the worm tube *Ditrupa,* forms a distinct band 4 m above the base. Small *Glycymeris* are common in a band 8 m above the base of the cycle. The upper part of the cycle comprises the clean, cross-bedded fine to medium sand of the **Portsmouth Member.** *Ophiomorpha* burrows are occasionally present in these sands. A conspicuous, well lithified ironstone band towards the base of the member forms a distinctive marker horizon (locality 2.4).

Much of **Cycle 4** (19.5 m) consists of a second series of cross-bedded sands, the **Whitecliff Member,** which are separated from the underlying Portsmouth Member by a thin sequence of bioturbated sandy muds containing occasional flint pebbles. It is, therefore, understandable that the two members were formerly grouped together in a single unit, the "Bagshot Sands". The top of the cycle is marked by a very prominent, although thin, conglomerate of well rounded black flint pebbles (locality 2.5). Until recently, this conglomerate was considered to represent the local base of the Bracklesham Group, but detailed stratigraphic correlation has shown that this actually lies 11 m higher up the succession, where muds of London Clay type give way to siltier, in part heterolithic, sediments.

The **Bracklesham Group** comprises four formations: the Wittering Formation (53 m), Earnley Sand (25 m), Marsh Farm Formation (13·5 m) and Selsey Sand (about 30 m) in ascending order. Transgressive/regressive cycles are recognisable, although they are somewhat different from those of the London Clay. Apart from the lowest cycle, which has a pebbly base and commences within the London Clay, cycle bases are marked by burrowed contacts. Deep green glauconitic sandy muds or sands, usually with an abundant marine fauna, characterise the lower parts of the cycles. The upper parts are heterolithic, interbedded muds (often lignitic), silts and sands, which are unfossiliferous except for a few poorly preserved leaves.

Cycle 1 (35 m) commences at the pebble bed within the London Clay on the southern margins of a deep gully. The lowest part, comprising massive silts and muds with relatively little glauconite and only occasional molluscan moulds, is poorly exposed. The upper part of the cycle (comprising the lowest part of the **Wittering Formation**) consists of heterolithic lignitic or glauconitic, laminated muds and sands, and some thicker, cross-bedded sands.

The base of **Cycle 2** (29 m) is marked by a bioturbated (burrowed) junction above which are some 14 m of glauconitic sandy and silty muds. Near the base are two prominent shell beds (Cardita Bed) (locality 2.6). The cycle is completed by heterolithic, thinly-bedded muds, lignitic muds, silts and sands. A massive lignite (1 m) with an underlying rootlet bed occurs about 7 m from the top of the cycle (locality 2.7). This is the Whitecliff Bay Bed, whose lateral equivalents can be recognised throughout much of the Hampshire. It is considered to represent a period of time when supratidal marshes occupied a large part of the Hampshire Basin area. It appears to coincide with a major regression consequent upon a global fall in sea-level.

The lower part of **Cycle 3** (38·5 m) equates with the **Earnley Sand**. At the base, glauconitic fine-grained sands rest with a sharp contact on the top of the Wittering Formation. The glauconitic sands of this cycle are very fossiliferous and contain *Venericor planicosta, Turritella* and other molluscs. About 20 m above the base, a very shelly bed contains numerous tests of the large foraminiferid *Nummulites laevigatus* (locality 2.8). The cycle is completed by the heterolithic association of sands, muds and lignites comprising the **Marsh Farm Formation.**

Cycle 4 (about 30 m) (coinciding with the **Selsey Sand**) differs from the earlier cycles in that it lacks any development of heterolithic, laminated facies in its upper part. Instead, it comprises glauconitic and non-glauconitic sands, silts and silty muds. The Cerithium giganteum Bed at the base of the cycle rests on a burrowed junction and contains *Campanile, Turritella, Cornulina,* etc. Almost at the top of the cycle is the patchily lithified, yellowish Tellina Sandstone.

At the top of the Selsey Sand is the Nummulites variolarius Bed, a sandy mud containing *Nummulites variolarius,* other foraminiferids, molluscs and the small coral *Turbinolia.* This may be visible on the southern side of the gully immediately south of the zigzag path (locality 2.9), although in recent years exposures here have deteriorated due to the installation of local "cliff protection". This bed represents a further transgression. Some authorities would place this bed within the Barton Clay on the basis of its lithology.

The **Barton Clay** (about 45 m) and the overlying **Chama Sand** (about 15 m) are poorly exposed in the cliff section, although two nummulite-rich horizons can sometimes be found by digging just south of the zigzag path (locality 2.10). *Nummulites prestwichianus* is common in a thin glauconitic sandy, whilst about 6 m higher *Nummulites rectus* occurs in a stiff bluish mud. The Barton Clay was deposited in a shallow, muddy shelf sea. The muddy and intensely bioturbated Chama Sand is occasionally visible immediately north of the zigzag path.

To the north of the zigzag path, the **Becton Sand** forms a near vertical cliff. It comprises mainly buff-coloured sands, sometimes cross-bedded or mottled and with occasional mud bands. In the upper part, the sand is cleaner with a few clay lenses and thin mud-pellet conglomerates. *Ophiomorpha* burrows occur sporadically at this level. The Becton Sand probably represents upper shoreface and beach conditions.

The junction between the Becton Sand and the **Headon Hill Formation** (just over 90 m) is exposed in the more northerly path descending the cliff (locality 2.11), where a sudden change from yellow sands to green muds is seen. The **Totland Bay Member** (8.2 m) comprises green muds, lignitic muds and muddy sands with a sandy ironstone near the middle. It contains a freshwater molluscan fauna, including *Viviparus, Galba* and *Planorbina,* except in the uppermost beds where the brackish water forms *Potamomya, Melanopsis* and *Theodoxus* occur. Most of the succeeding **Colwell Bay Member** (30 m) is weathered and decalcified and the detailed succession can only be demonstrated on fresh exposures. The unit contains three transgressive cycles. At the base is a deep brown sandy mud, the Brockenhurst Bed, which rests on an eroded and burrowed surface. This bed contains a large and diverse marine fauna including the molluscs *Ostrea, Venericor, Pelycora, Psammotaea* and, less commonly, corals and echinoids. The central part of the member comprises yellow, muddy fine sands with occasional molluscs. Above, come green sandy muds full of shells including *Pelycora, Ostrea, Corbula* and *Potamides* (the Venus Bed). The member is completed by a bright green mud with a sparse fauna including *Corbicula.* The **Cliff End Member** (14.8 m) is characterised by grey-green and brown muds with layers of *Potamomya* and *Viviparus.* Much of the remaining Headon Hill Formation succession has been affected by slips, but the general character of the sequence can usually be established. The **Lacey's Farm Limestone Member** (6.7 m) is here represented by almost unfossiliferous green to white marls with a particularly distinctive thin creamy-white silty limestone near the middle. This is followed by the **Fishbourne Member** (10.7 m) comprising grey and green thinly laminated muds with freshwater molluscs, ostracods and fish debris. The succeeding **Osborne Marls Member** (10.7 m) is characterised by unfossiliferous red and green, colour-mottled muds. The formation is completed by the **Seagrove Bay Member** (9.5 m) comprising green muds with thin siltstones and sandstones, and a thin, dark lignitic clay at the top.

Within the Headon Hill Formation, only the Brockenhurst Bed is fully marine, with the Venus Bed representing higher brackish salinities. Above the Colwell Bay Member, salinities fluctuated from brackish to freshwater. The variously mottled, often red-coloured sediments of the Osborne Marls Member reflect times of soil formation in an area with a fluctuating water table.

The **Bembridge Limestone** (8.5 m) is well exposed at the northern end of the bay. Where first seen (locality 2.12), it dips steeply northwards but, within a very short distance, the dip decreases to a low angle. The formation consists mainly of pale brown to white fossiliferous limestones and marls. *Galba* and *Planorbina* are abundant as moulds in many of the limestones, whilst land gastropods are less common. Charophyte oögonia are abundant in places. These limestones were deposited in a shallow freshwater environment.

The succession comprises a series of sedimentary cycles. These commence with an erosive base followed by a thin, intraformational conglomerate. In the lower part of the formation, where the cycles are best developed, the latter is succeeded by marls and marly limestones which pass up into hard limestones. The tops of these hard limestones may be pseudo-brecciated or nodular. Such cycles represent varying water depths and periodic exposure.

A thin development of grey, green and black muds with *Corbicula* towards the middle of the formation represents brackish water conditions and thus a minor transgressive phase. The cycles in the sequence above this level lack the marly component and are less easily recognisable. The uppermost bed is a white marly limestone, which in places is markedly conglomeratic.

The **Bembridge Marls Member** (34 m) of the **Bouldnor Formation** consists of muds and silts with occasional thin sands and limestones. Its base is marked by a pale green marl containing poorly preserved *Polymesoda* and *Potamides,* indicative of a rise in salinity. This bed is a local feature not seen at other localities and is usually well exposed at Black Rock (locality 2.13). It is overlain by the thin Bembridge Oyster Bed, a pale grey sand with abundant drifted and comminuted *Ostrea,* relatively few other molluscs and flint pebbles. This bed represents a widespread transgression, although the restricted fauna indicates that the waters were brackish rather than fully marine. It can be traced northwards into Howgate Bay where, at beach level, it becomes patchily lithified. Just above the Oyster Bed is a distinctive, discontinuous, buff, very fine-grained limestone. This is the lateral equivalent of the so-called Insect Limestone (see Itinerary 19), although insect remains are very rare at this locality. **Note that Black Rock Point may sometimes be difficult to pass at high tide depending on the state of the cliffs.**

The remainder of the Bembridge Marls Member consists mainly of muds and silts, although occasional thin limestones, sands and sandstones occur. The lower part contains brackish water molluscs such as *Polymesoda*. Higher up, the fauna is dominated by freshwater gastropods such as *Viviparus*, although the presence of other gastropods, such as *Melanopsis*, at some horizons suggests that the waters occasionally became slightly brackish. This upper part of the sequence consists of a number of fining-upward cycles, each commencing with a pale siltstone or fine sandstone. The base of one of the cycles is the source of slabs of thin siltstone found on the beach in Howgate Bay and on the cliff face itself. These slabs exhibit a variety of sedimentary and biogenic structures including gutter casts, tool marks, oriented crack fills, gypsum pseudomorphs, tracks and trails. **The upper levels of the succession may be difficult to reach after wet weather because of mudflows.** In Howgate Bay, the Bouldnor Formation disappears beneath Quaternary gravels (see Itinerary 1).

3. Sandown Bay North

The cliff section between Yaverland and Culver Cliff at the northern end of Sandown Bay (Figure 9) exposes almost the whole of the local Cretaceous succession. In recent years, parts of the succession have become obscured by landslips but it is possible to see much of the Wessex and Vectis Formations, most of the Lower Greensand Group and the Lower Chalk Formation. The section lies on the northern limb of the Sandown Anticline and there is a gradual increase in dip from about 10°N at Yaverland to nearly vertical at eastern end of Culver Cliff. **It is preferable to commence the traverse on a falling tide, particularly if the upper parts of the succession are to be examined. Cars and minibuses can be parked in the public car park opposite Sandown Zoo (611849). However, it should be noted that the area is a popular tourist centre and parking spaces are limited in the summer season. Walking distance, including the return, about 6 km. The traverse below Culver Cliff involves rough scrambling over a boulder-strewn foreshore.**

References. Casey (1961), Gale *et al.* (1996), Kennedy (1969), Lord & Bown (1987), Owen (1971), Radley (1994a,b, 1995), Ruffell (1988), Ruffell & Harvey (1993), Simpson (1985), Wach & Ruffell (1991).

Sandown Bay North

Descend to the beach from the car park. The uppermost 50 m or so of the Wessex Formation can be seen in the low cliff and intermittent foreshore exposures over a distance of about 900 m north of the car park. The hinge zone of the Sandown Anticline can sometimes be traced in exposures in the intertidal zone immediately south of the car park when storms have removed the normal cover of beach sand. The limited exposures reveal red mottled, floodplain mudstones interbedded with pink, medium-grained bioturbated sandstones, the latter probably representing crevasse-splay deposits.

Immediately north of the car park the first of a number of plant debris beds may be visible. This comprises grey silts and muds with comminuted plant debris and compressed, carbonised wood. Between the northern end of the car park and the new slipway (locality 3.1), the low cliff reveals a $c.3.5$ m thick sequence of thin, pale, fine-grained sands or silts and reddish mudstones. The unit exhibits large-scale cross-bedding and is interpreted as a muddy point bar deposit. On the rare occasions when this bed is exposed on the foreshore, several horizons of tridactyl (three-toed) dinosaur footprints and trackways can be seen. In the cliff, the footprints are seen in section and can be recognised as localised soft sediment deformation structures.

North of the new slipway, the cliffs reveal sporadic exposures of red mottled mudstones with vertical rootlet traces. These mudstones were deposited by vertically accretion of suspended load from ponded flood waters on an alluvial floodplain. The mottling was produced secondarily by pedogenic (soil-forming) processes. Scattered through the succession are further relatively thin plant debris beds, comprising grey silts and muds containing abundant comminuted plant debris, fusain (fossil charcoal), crushed cones and compressed, carbonised wood. The wood is mainly coniferous but cycads and tree ferns are found occasionally. These beds are interpreted as the product of local storm events which deposited swept debris into shallow depressions on the alluvial plain. In addition to plant material, these units contain siderite concretions, freshwater bivalves, fish scales and teeth, and reptile bones. Many of the freshwater bivalves are articulated and in life position. The most frequently exposed plant debris beds are the group of three which occur about between 16·5 and 10·5 m below the top of the formation. These crop out in the cliff just before the first conspicuous landslip (locality 3.2; 61608516) and can be traced on the foreshore to the northeast (beneath the remnants of the old sea wall of Purbeck limestone blocks) on the odd occasions when the beach shingle has been scoured away.

Further northeast, large blocks of pale grey, cross-laminated sandstone occur on the beach. These are derived from a bed about 7·5 m below the top of the formation. This unit can be traced in sporadic exposures behind the landslip. It appears to be another example of a crevasse-splay deposit. The bed exhibits soft

Sandown Bay North

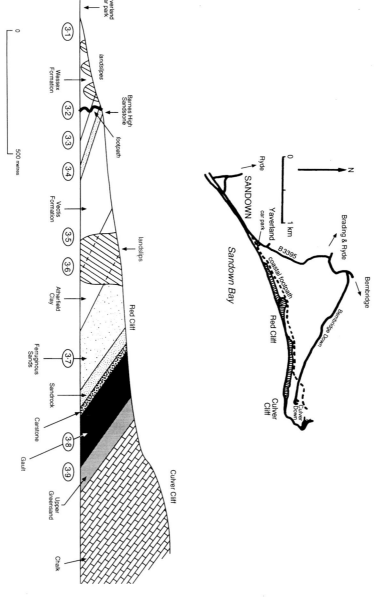

Figure 9. Location map and cliff profile from Yaverland to Culver Cliff.

sediment deformation and fallen blocks sometimes show distorted tridactyl dinosaur footprint casts on their undersides.

The junction between the Wessex Formation and the **Vectis Formation** (48 m) is marked by a conspicuous change from the dominantly red colour of the former to dark grey. This change is exposed at locality 3.3 (61788526) where the contact is seen to be a sharp scoured surface with a few indeterminate burrows penetrating down from the base of the Vectis Formation. This junction marks the transgression of the Vectis Formation lagoon over the Wessex Formation alluvial plain.

The Cowleaze Chine Member (about 10 m), the lowest division of the Vectis Formation, is usually poorly exposed. It consists of dark grey fissile muds with thin silt and fine-grained sand laminations, the latter becoming more frequent towards the top of the unit. Some beds contain the brackish water bivalve *Filosina gregaria.* A hard, buff to brown clay ironstone band about 4.5 m below the top of the member contains numerous moulds of the freshwater gastropod *Viviparus infracretacicus.* Blocks of this ironstone are usually common on the beach. The Cowleaze Chine Member is believed to have been deposited in as a shallow, fresh- to slightly brackish-water lagoon.

The **Barnes High Sandstone Member** (about 2.5 m) forms a low, but conspicuous, cliff of yellow sandstone (locality 3.4). This is a coarsening upward unit with a gradational contact with the underlying Cowleaze Chine Member. Bioturbated dark grey muds and silts at the base are overlain by wavy interlaminations of muddy silt and silty fine sand which pass up in turn into lenticular and wavy bedded sands separated by thin mud drapes. These are succeeded by small-scale cross-bedded sands which occur in upward thickening sets. Larger scale cross-bedded sands with mud-draped troughs occur in the upper part of the unit. The top is marked by a rippled surface which usually forms a small ledge. The sands throughout this unit are stained and irregularly cemented by iron oxides. There are no body fossils, but some bedding surfaces reveal trace fossils. The origin of Barnes High Sandstone is uncertain but the current view is that it was deposited as a prograding lagoonal delta which was subject to some reworking by wave action.

The lower part of the succeeding **Shepherd's Chine Member** (50 m), is generally not well exposed but comprises interlaminated dark grey muds, pale silts and fine-grained sands arranged in repeated fining-upward units. Three thin coarse-grained cross-bedded sandstones occur within the lower 5 m of the unit. Higher parts of the sequence can usually be seen west of the large landslip immediately west of Red Cliff and in occasionally available foreshore exposures below the slip (locality 3.5). The anomalous steep westerly dip in the latter area is due to disturbance by the landslip. In this part of the Vectis Formation, the cycles are not well developed, the sequence consisting of dark grey to black muds with parallel silt or fine-grained sand laminations and small-scale cross-bedded microlenses. Many of the bedding planes in the fissile laminated mudstones are strewn with large numbers of ostracods. Four thin coquina (shell debris) limestones (10-20 cm thick) occur in the upper part of the member. Three are packed with mainly disarticulated valves of the brackish water bivalve *Filosina gregaria*. The thickest *Filosina* limestone, some 3 m below the top of the member, has layers of "beef" or cone-in-cone structure (fibrous calcite) on its upper and lower surfaces. The fourth limestone contains an assemblage dominated by disarticulated shells of the oyster *Ostrea distorta*. Blocks of these limestones are abundant on the beach. The coquinas were probably generated by storms sweeping across the shallow water lagoon. A thin brown clay ironstone with the freshwater gastropod *Viviparus* occurs about 7 m below the top of the member. Gutter casts (straight or sinuous narrow sandstone-filled erosional scours) are common in this part of the succession and were produced as a result of unidirectional scouring by storm-generated currents and subsequent infilling by suspended sediment during waning storm conditions or fair-weather currents.

The **Atherfield Clay Formation** (about 35 m), the lowest subdivision of the **Lower Greensand Group,** is involved in the landslip and its junction with the Vectis Formation is reached with difficulty on the western side of the large landslip east of Red Cliff. The basal **Perna Bed Member** (1.8 m) is, however, generally visible as a ridge of rock on the foreshore at low tide (locality 3.6) although its dip reflects recent landslipping. Under favourable conditions a complete sequence of the bed may be available for study. This unit marks the transgressive base of the Lower Greensand Group. A dark blue-grey sandy mud infilling burrows extending down up to 15 cm into the Vectis Formation occurs at its base. In places, there is a very thin, discontinuous layer of rolled bone fragments, fish teeth and phosphatic pebbles in a coarse quartz sand matrix, the Atherfield Bone-Bed. The bone fragments and fish teeth were derived from the underlying Wealden Group. The rest of the member comprises a blue-green, glauconitic, bioturbated, muddy calcareous coarse-grained sandstone. A rich fauna is recorded from this unit, including the bivalves *Mulletia mulleti, Aetostreon latissimum* and *Sphaera corrugata,* and the coral *Holocystis elegans.* The sandstone contains considerable numbers of phosphatic pebbles, including derived rolled phosphatised Kimmeridgian ammonites. The Perna Bed Member is interpreted as a reworked shelf-shoreline deposit.

The remainder of the Atherfield Clay comprises massive brown weathering, blue grey muds and sandy muds with flattened irregular brown clay-ironstone nodules in the lower part. The subdivisions recognised in Chale Bay are not easily distinguished here, but a 4 m band of bioturbated dark blue sandy mud and a

Sandown Bay North

brown sand just below the top of the unit is considered to represent the **Crackers Member.** Body fossils are uncommon but occasional pyritised examples of the ammonite *Deshayesites* may be found.

From this point onwards, the cliffs are vertical and a hard hat should always be worn. It is not advisable to work beneath the cliffs either after frost or heavy rain, when there is a constant rain of debris, sometimes quite large.

The greater part of Red Cliff (locality 3.7) comprises the **Ferruginous Sands Formation** (105 m), here virtually unfossiliferous, apart from trace fossils. The subdivision of the formation, possible at Chale Bay, is not easily achieved here except at the northern end of the cliff where beds equivalent to Members XII to XIV can be recognised. The basal contact is sharp with extensive burrowing into the underlying Atherfield Clay. The formation comprises alternations of glauconitic muddy sands and cleaner limonitic sands. Where unweathered, both lithologies contain high concentrations of glauconite. Weathering rapidly alters the glauconite to iron oxides and hydroxides. Hence the dominant red-brown colour of the sequence. Variation in the extent of weathering is probably controlled by clay, with high clay content inhibiting the process. At several horizons, concentrations of curious flat, often subangular, flakes of iron oxide occur. The origin of these is uncertain but it is possible that they were derived by subaerial erosion of iron-rich soils on an adjacent land area. A conspicuous bed of phosphatic pebbles about 10 to 15 cm thick occurs about 12 m below the top of the formation. This bed has yielded derived Jurassic fossils, including the Kimmeridgian ammonite *Pavlovia.*

The **Sandrock Formation** and the **Carstone Formation** are exposed at the northeastern end of Red Cliff. Both are affected by three small faults whose northerly downthrows cross the cliff face obliquely. The Sandrock Formation (about 28 m) consists mainly of thick units of white, yellow and brown fine- to medium-grained quartz sands. A dark grey laminated mud marks the base and a bed of similar lithology occurs about 10 m below the top. The whole succession is badly weathered and sedimentary structures are poorly preserved, except in the uppermost part where mud laminations, lenticular bedding and flaser bedding occur. The Carstone Formation (about 22 m) is a red-brown ferruginous coarse-grained, poorly sorted sandstone with some phosphatic concretions. It has a sharp erosional contact with the underlying Sandrock. A pebble bed occurs about 6 m below the top of the formation.

The **Gault Clay** (28.4 m) crops out in the hollow between Red Cliff and Culver Cliff (locality 3.8). It is usually largely obscured by slumping or vegetation but, where visible, comprises a blue-grey to blue-black sandy and silty clay. The trace fossil *Chondrites* is common at some horizons but body fossils are rare, although a pale brown band 4 m above the base contains crushed ammonites *(Hoplites)*. The junction between the Gault and the **Upper Greensand** (about 30 m) together with the lower beds of the latter are usually concealed by slips. When exposed, the contact is seen to be gradational, with some 4.5 m of interbedded blue-grey silty or sandy clays and grey-buff silts and fine-grained sands. Above these "Passage Beds" come some 20 m of pale grey-green glauconitic fine-grained sandstones and siltstones with irregular layers of calcareous concretions. These are exposed in Culver Cliff to the east of the Gault hollow (locality 3.9). Brown phosphatic concretions occur throughout but are particularly abundant at the top. This sequence is followed by the Chert Beds, 1.8 m of grey-green sandstones with lenticular masses of chert. The top of the Upper Greensand is formed by 3 m of grey-green glauconitic fine-grained sands and silts with both siliceous and calcareous concretions as well as phosphatic nodules. In the lower part of the formation sedimentary structures are not preserved but in the upper beds, glauconite-rich laminations become conspicuous and there are some indications of small-scale cross-bedding. The laminations are compacted around the concretions suggesting an early diagenetic origin for them. Fossils are uncommon, but the oysters *Exogyra obliquata* and *Pycnodonte vesicularis* together with the serpulid worm *Rotularia concava* can usually be found in the upper part. Brown phosphatic concretions occur throughout, but become more common upwards. Some are clearly phosphatised fossils.

The remainder of the itinerary concerns the Chalk Group, although the upper part is currently difficult to examine *in situ*. **The Chalk Group of Culver Cliff is badly shattered and rock falls are frequent, especially in the winter and early spring. Great care should be exercised when proceeding along this part of the section and no attempt should be made to climb the cliffs. This part of the itinerary should only be undertaken on a falling tide.** Much of the base of the cliff is obscured by fallen material but it is usually possible to follow the succession in broad outline.

The **Lower Chalk Formation** commences with the **Glauconitic Marl,** which can be examined *in situ* or in numerous fallen blocks. It is an unbedded, intensely bioturbated, dark green, calcareous glauconitic sandstone. The contact with the Upper Greensand is a marked non-sequence representing a time gap of about 1 to 2 million years. The junction is extensively burrowed, so much so that concretions at the top of the Upper Greensand are almost completely surrounded by Glauconitic Marl, some burrows penetrating as much as 0·5 m below the contact. The trace fossil *Thalassinoides* is particularly abundant at this level. Dark brown phosphatic pebbles are common at the base of the Glauconitic Marl, most of them being fragments of phosphatised sponges.

Sandown Bay North

About 50 m east of the point where the Upper Greensand descends to the beach a magnificent view of the Lower Chalk Formation sequence in the cliff can be obtained from the foreshore platform. The whole succession is conspicuously rhythmic with white harder beds containing more carbonate alternating with grey, slightly softer, more clay-rich marls. The sharp boundary between the darker Chalk Marl and the overlying, lighter Grey Chalk is clearly visible in the cliff. Detailed inspection of this part of the Chalk Group is best undertaken on the foreshore when it has been stripped clear of sand and seaweed by storm action. However, the general character of the lithologies can examined in fallen blocks.

The **Chalk Marl** comprises mainly alternations of thick blue-grey mottled marl and thin nodular grey hard chalk. Dark brown phosphatic and pyritic nodules are common throughout. Fossils are abundant particularly sponges *(Exanthesis)*, bivalves *(Pycnodonte, Inoceramus, Plicatula)*, ammonites *(Schloenbachia, Acanthoceras, Mantelliceras)*, brachiopods *(Orbirhynchia, Concinnithyris)* and echinoids *(Holaster)*. About 18 m above the base of Chalk Marl, there is a marked lithological change where the hard chalk/marl interbeds are replaced by massive grey to white hard chalk with only thin grey marl seams. This change marks the base of the **Grey Chalk.** Marls in the beds immediately below the junction contain abundant examples of the brachiopod *Orbirhynchia mantelliana.* The whole Grey Chalk succession is intensely burrowed and pyrite nodules occur throughout. Fossils present include bivalves *(Inoceramus, Pycnodonte, Pecten)*, occasional ammonites *(Acanthoceras, Austinoceras)*, and echinoids *(Holaster)*. Two prominent burrowed erosion surfaces are visible, one 10 m below the top of the unit and the second at the junction with the overlying Plenus Marls. Throughout the Chalk Marl and Grey Chalk, there are abundant signs of compaction in the form of marl flasers and modification of burrows plus numerous calcite-filled tectonic fractures (crystal slickensides). The **Plenus Marls,** a conspicuous band of blue-grey marl and pale grey chalk about 4 m thick, mark the top of the Lower Chalk Formation and, being relatively soft, have been eroded to form a small re-entrant in the cliff line. Characteristic fossils of this unit, including the belemnite *Actinocamax plenus,* are present here. **Beyond this point, the section becomes progressively more difficult to traverse over the rock debris which litters the base of the cliff.** The higher beds can be examined in fallen blocks and in occasional clear exposures. Fossils are difficult to locate on fresh surfaces, but are reasonably common where the rock has been air weathered.

The **White Chalk Formation** succession commences with the nodular chalks of the **Ranscombe Member** which, in its upper part, contains abundant specimens of the inoceramid bivalve *Mytiloides mytiloides*. The green- and orange-tinted Ogbourne Hardground (Spurious Chalk Rock of Rowe, 1908) which marks the base of the **St. Margaret's Member** can clearly be seen weathered out in the cliff. Higher parts of this member can be examined in fallen blocks. Particularly distinctive beds include a pinkish-brown, very well lithified hardground containing abundant *Micraster decipiens,* which is equivalent to the Top Rock found in the area north of London, and a bed containing great numbers of the distinctive small bryozoan *Bicavea.*

A return can now be made to the starting point along the beach. Do not attempt to round Culver Point; Whitecliff Bay is not accessible along the base of the cliff even at extreme low tide.

4. Central Sandown Bay

The cliffs between Sandown and Shanklin expose the central part of the **Ferruginous Sands Formation.** The exposures lie on the southern limb of the Sandown Anticline, the beds dipping at a shallow angle, generally less than 5° to the south, this being interrupted by a low amplitude anticline between Little Stairs and Shanklin Chine. Deep weathering and the general rarity of fossils makes correlation between this section and that of the type section in Chale Bay (Itinerary 7) uncertain. However, it appears that the equivalent to the succession between the unnamed Member VI and the New Walpen Chine Member is represented. The base of the cliff has been protected from marine erosion by a massive sea wall and this has resulted in a general deterioration of the exposures. Furthermore, some sections of the cliff have been obscured by further anti-erosion works. Nonetheless, the section here reveals some features which are either absent or difficult of access at other Ferruginous Sands localities.

The itinerary which follows commences at the southern end of Sandown Esplanade (596838), but it may be carried out in the reverse direction by starting at the northern end of Shanklin Esplanade (588819) if more convenient. Cars can be parked at either access point, although this can be difficult during the summer season. There is no provision at either point for the parking of coaches. The cliff section is accessible at all states of the tide but a low tide is essential for the examination of the foreshore exposures in the Little Stairs area. Walking distance about 6 km, including the return to the starting point.

References. Casey (1961), Wach & Ruffell (1991).

Immediately south of the end of Sandown Esplanade (Figure 10), the lower part of the cliff exposes greenish-grey muddy sands which become darker and muddier upwards. These appear to be equivalent to the unnamed **Member VI** and **Whale Chine Member** of the Chale Bay section. There are two prominent and several minor bands of ferruginous concretions within the sequence. The top of the unit is marked by a discontinuous layer of ferruginous concretions and a

Central Sandown Bay

Figure 10a. Location Map.

spring line marked by a narrow zone of vegetation. It reaches beach level about 230 m south of the bottom of Lake Stairs. Fossils are scarce in this unit, but lignite and poorly preserved moulds of the oyster *Aetostreon* are sometimes found. Near Lake Stairs, ammonites (*Tropaeum, Cheloniceras, Dufrenoyia*) have occasionally been found in ferruginous concretions.

The second unit in the section consists of about 15 m of brown, yellow and grey-green glauconitic muddy sands which become darker sandy muds towards the top. This appears to correlate with the unnamed **Member VIII** in Chale Bay. Colour mottling due to bioturbation occurs throughout the unit. Two prominent sets of large-scale cross-bedding occur near the middle of the unit. The upper unit is single-storied and disappears northwards. The lower one is multi-storied in the south, but becomes single-storied northwards. The foresets of both sets dip southwards. In places, the foresets are over-steepened and exhibit slumping and/or synsedimentary faulting. A good example of these features is accessible about half way up Lake Stairs (locality 4.1). Here, the slumping is directed to the southwest and in the same direction as the palaeocurrent as indicated by the foresets. These sands are interpreted as sandwaves on a tidally influenced shelf. The deformation of the foresets was produced by lateral shearing. This could have been generated either by seismic shock or by the surface drag produced by bedform migration over water-saturated sediment. The top of the unit is indicated by a narrow vegetated ledge which reaches beach level about 180 m north of Little Stairs. About 3 m below the top of the unit is a band of large

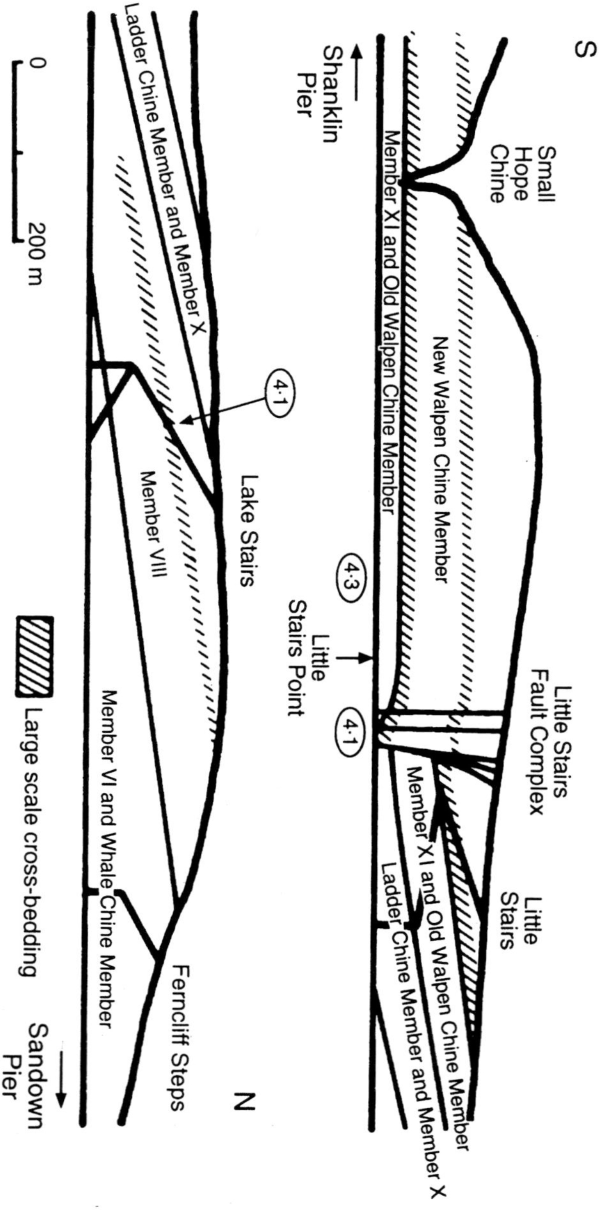

Figure 10b. Cliff profile from Sandown Esplanade to Shanklin Esplanade.

discoidal concretions which is occasionally exposed on the foreshore at low tide. These concretions occasionally contain impressions of large ammonites (*Tropaeum, Epicheloniceras*).

The next unit is believed to be the local equivalent of the **Ladder Chine Member** and the unnamed **Member X** of the Chale Bay section. It comprises 9.1 m of blue-grey muddy sands at base which pass up into green-brown and brown coarse glauconitic sands. A prominent bed of ironstone occurs about 3 m above the base. The whole unit is extensively bioturbated and no sedimentary structures are preserved. About 100 m south of Little Stairs, rotted concretions occur 1.2 m below the ironstone band. Some of these concretions contain fossils including the ammonite *Epicheloniceras*. In the uppermost 3 m of the unit, moulds of the oyster *Aetostreon* are fairly common. A reef of this part of the succession containing clusters of *Aetostreon* and *Lopha* is occasionally seen on the foreshore opposite Small Hope Chine.

At the base of the next unit there is a sudden change from the brown sands to dark blue-grey glauconitic muddy sands. These dark sands probably equate with the unnamed **Member XI** and the **Old Walpen Chine Member** in Chale Bay. They form a prominent feature in the cliff in the neighbourhood of Little Stairs and pass up into dark grey-green sandy muds, the whole being about 7.5 m thick. Mud lenticles and cross-bedded lenses occur near the base of the unit. On either side of the third breakwater south of Little Stairs Point, a number of arcuate units of interlaminated glauconitic, pebbly coarse-grained sandstone and mud are usually exposed on the foreshore at low tide (locality 4.3). In plan view, they appear to be very large-scale trough cross-bedded units with very variable trends. They apparently lie within the lower part of the unit. These sandstones are interpreted as a sandwave complex deposited in a tidal estuary eroded in muddy glauconitic shelf sediments. In the upper half of the sequence, pebbles of quartz occur. This pebbly muddy greensand forms the base of the cliff at Little Stairs Point, where it contains small fragments of wood.

About 150 m south of Little Stairs, a complex of extension faults occurs (locality 4.2). These have a combined downthrow to the south of about 20 m. The fault planes are normally obscured by rock fall debris but the position of the complex is indicated by a re-entrant in the cliff.

The final unit in the section forms the upper part of the cliff from Little Stairs to Shanklin Chine. This unit is equivalent to the **New Walpen Chine Member** in Chale Bay. It consists of brown, green and grey-green muddy sands. There are two conspicuous horizons of large-scale cross-bedding, both with southerly dipping foresets. In the area around Little Stairs Point, blocks of orange ferruginous sand, coming from a lenticular mass in the upper part of the unit, sometimes occur. These have yielded the bivalves *Aetostreon* and *Lopha*, the echinoid *Trochotiara* and bryozoans. A short distance beyond Little Stairs Point, the base of the cliff becomes inaccessible but the general character of the unit can be appreciated from the footpath.

Beyond Small Hope Chine, the cliff is largely hidden by buildings, although the sequence can be followed by eye southwards. It is therefore best to discontinue the traverse at this point and either return to Sandown or alternatively walk south along Shanklin Esplanade to the starting point of Itinerary 5.

5. Knock Cliff and Luccombe Bay

The cliffs at the southern end of Sandown Bay expose a Lower Greensand Group sequence ranging from the uppermost part of the Ferruginous Sands Formation to the basal part of the Carstone. The Ferruginous Sands here are relatively fossiliferous and the Sandrock is rich in both trace fossils and sedimentary structures.

The itinerary commences at the southern end of Shanklin Esplanade (585811), where cars and minibuses can be parked, except at the height of the summer season. Coaches can make temporary stops for unloading but cannot be parked. Total walking distance about 6 km including the return to Shanklin. Horse and Yellow Ledges can only be rounded only within about 3 hours either side of low tide, and this itinerary should therefore only be attempted on a falling tide. It is no longer possible to exit Luccombe Bay via the footpath up Luccombe Chine.

References. Casey (1961), Dike (1972b), Middlemiss (1962).

From the southern end of Shanklin Esplanade the general features of the sequence are visible to the south in Knock Cliff (Figure 11), in which the gentle southerly dip of the beds is apparent. The lower part of the cliff is composed of the Ferruginous Sands Formation, usually partly obscured in the cliff face by a veneer of clay washed down from above. The first terrace in the cliff face marks the base of the Sandrock Formation which forms the remainder of the cliff.

Walk southwards to the entrance to Shanklin Chine (locality 5.1). The chine is eroded in the upper part of the **Ferruginous Sands Formation.** The lowest part of the chine is cut in deeply weathered glauconitic sands which represent the uppermost beds of the **Old Walpen Chine Member** in Chale Bay. These are overlain by a prominent pebble bed, obscured by beach huts at this point, but usually visible at beach level about 350 m to the south. Blocks of the

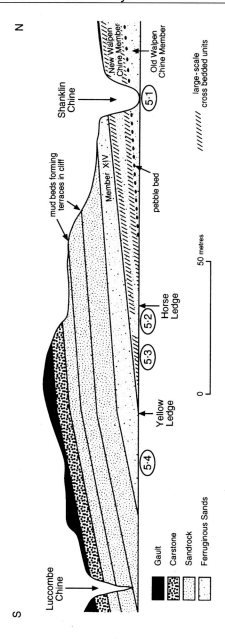

Figure 11. Cliff profile from Shanklin Chine to Luccombe Bay.

Knock Cliff and Luccombe Bay

conglomerate may also be found on the beach in this area. This conglomerate marks the base of the **New Walpen Chine Member.** It is a polymictic (mixed-rock) conglomerate, containing well-rounded to subangular, granule to cobble grade pebbles of quartz (often green-stained), darker siliceous rocks and sandstones set in a ferruginous sand matrix. The conglomerate rests on a scoured surface and marks a transgressive lag.

The bulk of the New Walpén Chine Member here is usually obscured by a veneer of clay washed down from above. Clean exposures reveal dark grey-green to blue-green glauconitic muddy sandstones, usually intensely bioturbated. However, the basal 2 m or so consists of interbedded grey muds and grey-green glauconitic silts which are occasionally seen on the foreshore, where the top contains carbonised plant debris. The top of this basal unit is cut by an erosion surface upon which rests a second thin polymictic conglomerate. This is also sometimes exposed on the foreshore. This conglomerate contains a mixture of quartz and glauconitic sandstone pebbles in a glauconitic coarse-grained sand matrix. It passes up, via a pebbly glauconitic sand, into green and blue-green glauconitic muddy sands. A large-scale cross-bedded band with southerly dipping foresets occurs about 5 m above the pebble bed in the chine. A reddish-brown sandstone with a prominent large-scale cross-bedded horizon at the bottom forms the upper part of Shanklin Chine. The oyster *Aetostreon* occurs singly or in bands throughout this sequence which is broadly interpreted as a shallow water shelf deposit.

Continue southwards towards Horse Ledge. On the beach just before the ledge are masses of ironstone, some containing very clear burrows, and dark cindery-looking boulders packed with the moulds of bivalves (*Thetironia, Pterotrigonia, Senis*) and gastropods (*Anchura, Gyrodes*). These boulders have come from the unnamed **Member XIV** of the Ferruginous Sands Formation which is inaccessible at this point. Also present on the beach are numerous fragments of fossil wood derived from the Sandrock Formation.

A particularly significant horizon in the New Walpen Chine Member lies about 8 m above the base of the unit and forms the foot of Shanklin Point and the reef known as Horse Ledge (locality 5.2). It consists of a very dark green, glauconitic muddy sandstone with small-scale cross-bedding and small burrows. The top of this bed is relatively hard and is overlain by a very fossiliferous bed about 60 cm thick. The latter contains clusters of the brachiopod *Rhynchonella parvirostris,* bivalves (*Aetostreon làtissima* and *Vectella morrisi*), bryozoa (*Siphodictyum*), serpulid worm tubes and echinoids (*Toxaster, Phyllobrissus*). The "nests" of brachiopods are interpreted as life assemblages. The hard band is interpreted as a firmground produced by erosion and winnowing during a period of non-deposition. The relatively firm surface created was then colonised by benthic

Knock Cliff and Luccombe Bay

organisms, in some places resulting in the construction of brachiopod and bryozoan mounds.

South of Horse Ledge, the succession is continued by sparsely fossiliferous dark green glauconitic muddy sands. About halfway between Horse Ledge and Yellow Ledge (locality 5.3), the large-scale cross-bedded unit seen at Shanklin Chine reaches the base of the cliff. It is overlain by brown sands with irregular discontinuous harder layers passing up into green glauconitic coarse-grained sand with scattered ironstone pebbles and isolated examples of the oyster *Aetostreon latissima.* This group of rocks is usually exposed on the foreshore to the north of Yellow Ledge and correlates with the unnamed Member XIV in Chale Bay. The interbedded blue-grey muddy glauconitic sands and grey fine-grained quartz sands which occur above contain hard dark brown, cindery-looking, phosphatic concretions enclosing abundant external and internal moulds of bivalves (*Thetironia, Pterotrigonia, Panopaea, Gervillella*), gastropods (*Globularia, Anchura*) and brachiopods (*"Rhynchonella"*). The bed comes down to beach level about 250 m south of Horse Ledge and forms Yellow Ledge. Although the concretions can only be examined *in situ* near Yellow Ledge, numerous fallen examples occur on the beach below Knock Cliff. The Ferruginous Sands succession is completed by dark grey sandy mud and muddy sand with a ferruginous claystone band near the middle.

Luccombe Bay is entered once Yellow Ledge is rounded. From here southwards to Luccombe Chine the cliff is composed almost entirely of the **Sandrock Formation** (about 40 m). The base of the formation is hidden by the debris which covers the terrace which reaches beach level about 300 m north of Luccombe Chine. The Sandrock sequence here contains three coarsening-upward units, the main characters of which can be seen in the largely inaccessible cliffs and in large fallen blocks on the beach just south of Yellow Ledge (locality 5.4). The lowest of these units (about 10 m thick) comprises dark grey-green pebbly and sandy mud grading up into pale grey bioturbated fine-grained sands with a quartz pebble bed at the top. The sands contain the distinctive large mud-pellet-lined burrow *Ophiomorpha.* The pebble bed contains clasts of black pebbly sandstone, phosphatic nodules, considerable quantities of rolled wood fragments and, less commonly, cones. This horizon is the source of all the fossil wood found on the beach between Shanklin and Luccombe Chine. Most is coniferous but cycad wood also occurs and almost all are extensively bored by the shipworm *Terebrimya.* This pebble bed can be reached with difficulty by climbing up the tumbled cliffs at the mouth of Luccombe Chine where the bed is about 3 m above beach level. **This should not be attempted after prolonged wet weather and great care is necessary in this area at all times.**

The Western Undercliff

The second coarsening-upward unit (about 19 m thick) consists of very glauconitic dark-green sandy mud and muddy fine sand which passes up into pale grey fine- to medium-grained quartz sands. The latter contain a variety of sedimentary structures including flat-bedding, large- and small-scale cross-bedding, ripple marks (often with clay drapes) and herring-bone cross-bedding. Some horizons are extensively bioturbated and *Ophiomorpha* burrows may be abundant. The uppermost unit comprises a glauconitic, muddy fine-grained sand which grades up into white, grey and yellow medium- to coarse-grained sands. The latter pass laterally southwards into lenticular and flaser bedded sands and muds. The Sandrock was deposited within an estuarine and tidal flat complex.

The red-brown **Carstone Formation** can be seen at the top of the cliff on either side of Luccombe Chine. It is inaccessible here, but the blocks of rusty brown, large-scale cross-bedded coarse-grained sandstone which occur on the beach throughout Luccombe Bay are derived from this unit.

The return to Shanklin can best be made by retracing the route northwards along the beach.

6. The Western Undercliff (Binnel Bay to Rocken End)
The main objective of this itinerary (Figure 12) is to investigate the solid geology of the upper part of the Lower Greensand Group, Gault, Upper Greensand and Lower Chalk. There are also some features which relate to the mass movements which were responsible for the formation of the Undercliff.

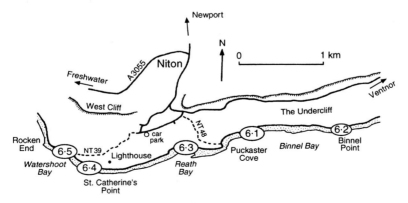

Figure 12. Location map for the western Undercliff area, Itinerary 6.

The Western Undercliff

There is limited parking for cars and minibuses, but not for coaches, in the road adjacent to the Buddle Inn, Niton (503757). This itinerary should only be undertaken on a falling tide. Walking distance about 4 km over paths, boulder-strewn foreshore and roads.

References. Hutchinson (1987), Kennedy (1969), Owen (1971), Preece (1986), Wach & Ruffell (1991).

From the Buddle Inn, walk eastwards along the coast road for about 500 m and take footpath NT48 down to the shore at the western end of Binnel Bay, known as Puckaster Cove. In the low cliffs east of here (locality 6.1) there are readily accessible exposures of the **Sandrock Formation.** The sequences here are dominated by grey-green glauconitic and pale grey quartz sands which exhibit a variety of sedimentary structures including small and large-scale cross-bedding, herringbone cross-bedding, graded bedding, mud drapes, flaser bedding and mud flake conglomerates. There are also some black laminated muds which exhibit lenticular and flaser bedding. There is great diversity of trace fossils, including vertical tube-like burrows (*Skolithos*), mud-pellet lined burrows (*Ophiomorpha*), bivalve escape traces and irregular tangles and blebs of more or less glauconitic sand (*Macaronichnus*). The Sandrock was deposited within an estuarine-tidal flat environment.

At Binnel Point (52537579; locality 6.2) the debris aprons forming the toe of the coastal landslip complex of the western Undercliff reach beach level. The low cliffs consist of a fragmented and chaotic mass of boulders produced by mass movements, such as rockfalls and debris flows, interspersed with mudflows. The boulders have varied stratigraphic provenance and several different lithologies can be recognised. These include chert and green-grey glauconitic sands, some with abundant oysters, from the highest part of the Upper Greensand and dark green, very glauconitic, calcareous sandstones from the Glauconitic Marl at the base of the Lower Chalk Formation. Dark brown soils found within the landslip debris apron contain land gastropods, occasional marine shells, some mammalian remains and charcoal. The marine molluscs, the larger mammal species and charcoal probably represent midden remains and a radiocarbon age of about 4500 years obtained from the charcoal indicates that the soils date from the Neolithic.

West of Puckaster Cove, in Reeth Bay (locality 6.3), a lower horizon within the Sandrock shows intensely burrowed muddy, darker sands. The blocks of very coarse, red-brown ferruginous sandstone littering the beach in Reeth Bay have fallen from the overlying **Carstone.** These occasionally yield casts and moulds of fossils in this area, including rare ammonites (*Sonneratia, Cleoniceras*).

Chale Bay

Just west of the slipway, the debris aprons forming the toe of the coastal landslip complex of the western Undercliff once more reach beach level. The debris here, as at Binnel Point, contains blocks from both the Upper Greensand and the Glauconitic Marl. The low cliffs of landslip debris continue to beyond St. Catherine's Point. Soil horizons, similar to those seen at Binnel Point, have been found west of St. Catherine's Lighthouse (locality 6.4). They contain land molluscs and large pieces of wood and logs, yielding radiocarbon ages of between about 4000 and 4500 years, that is Neolithic. Both here and at Binnel Point the soils represent a period of stability, soil formation and woodland development before the onset of a major phase of mass movement which buried them, possibly in the Iron Age (For the further significance of localities 6.2 and 6.4, see Itinerary 8d).

Beneath St. Catherine's Lighthouse and west towards Watershoot Bay and Rocken End (locality 6.5), the beach consists of a mass of boulders, some very large, derived from landslip debris. These boulders consist of Chalk Marl, Glauconitic Marl and Upper Greensand. **The Upper Greensand** blocks consist of pale grey-green to buff glauconitic siltstones with lines of pale brown calcareous or grey chert concretions. **The Glauconitic Marl** is a buff sandy marl with numerous dark brown phosphatic nodules. The junction between these two units is best seen on wave-washed blocks. At the base of the Glauconitic Marl is a conglomerate of bored, phosphatised and glauconitised pebbles and cobbles derived from the top of the Upper Greensand set in a glauconitic sandy matrix. This conglomerate rests on a burrowed Upper Greensand surface, its sandy matrix being piped down about 0·5 m into the Upper Greensand in large cylindrical burrows. Many of the phosphatic nodules within the Glauconitic Marl are recognisable as fossils and there is a very rich fauna including ammonites (for example, species of *Hypoturrilites, Idiohamites, Mantelliceras* and *Schloenbachia*), sponges (*Stauronema*), bivalves, gastropods and brachiopods. These fossils are best seen on the air-weathered surfaces. The **Chalk Marl,** as elsewhere on the Island, consists of alternations of fossiliferous white limestone and grey marls.

Return to the Buddle Inn via footpath NT37 running past Knowles Farm and the minor road running northeast.

7. Chale Bay

This itinerary examines the type section of the Lower Greensand Group between Atherfield and Rocken End. The beds dip about 3° NW in Chale Bay and as a consequence the Lower Greensand is exposed over a distance of about 5 km.

There are only a few access points to this section, the best being Shepherd's Chine at the western end (roadside verge parking at 451799), Whale Chine,

Chale Bay

towards the centre of the section (car park at **470784**) and the footpath past Knowles Farm (**497754**) at the eastern end. In recent years access via Whale Chine has frequently been impossible after winter storms and it is therefore advisable to check locally before using this route. If the weather is dry, the beach can also be reached from the coastal path near the Coastguard Station at Atherfield Point (**451790**) or by descending the landslips at Blackgang (**497760**), although neither of these routes is suitable for a party. Ladder, New Walpen, Old Walpen and Blackgang Chines cannot be used for access since at their lower ends there are sheer drops to the beach.

The Chale Bay area can be very dangerous and should be avoided during gales. The cliffs are vertical, cliff falls are frequent and a hard hat should always be worn here. It is not advisable to work beneath the cliffs either after frost or heavy rain, when there is a constant rain of debris, sometimes quite large. Atherfield Point and the Blackgang Chine area can only be passed at low tide. Large rockfalls, landslides or mudflows can isolate sections of the beach elsewhere and create a hazard on a rising tide. Great care should be therefore be taken regarding tides and it is recommended that the itinerary be commenced on a falling tide. The total walking distance is about 12 km. Given sufficient time and suitable tides, the whole of the gently easterly dipping sequence can be examined in a single day. However, it may be more convenient to split the itinerary into two parts, using Whale Chine as a convenient starting point. The examination of the southeastern part of the section could be linked with itinerary 6 and the examination of the western part of the bay with Itinerary 9.

References. Casey (1961), Dike (1972b), Fitton (1847), Hutchinson, Chandler & Bromhead (1981), Middlemiss (1962), Simpson (1985), Wach & Ruffell (1991).

Descend to the beach via Shepherd's Chine and walk eastwards past the Vectis Formation exposure (see Itinerary 9) to Atherfield Point (locality 7.1). From here the general relationships of the gently easterly dipping Lower Greensand Group succession (Figures 13 & 14) in Chale Bay can be appreciated. In the foreground is the grey Atherfield Clay Formation, whilst to the east most of the cliffs are eroded in the brown Ferruginous Sands Formation. In the distance, the pale bands of the Sandrock Formation can be seen around Blackgang. It may be possible to distinguish the deep red-brown of the Carstone Formation and the dark blue-grey of the Gault Clay in the upper part of the cliffs east of Blackgang Chine. Finally, pale grey Upper Greensand forms the prominent Gore Cliff.

Five subdivisions can be recognised within the **Atherfield Clay Formation** (about 53 m) in Chale Bay. At the base of the formation is the **Perna Bed Member** (1.5 m), usually well exposed at the foot of the landslips west of

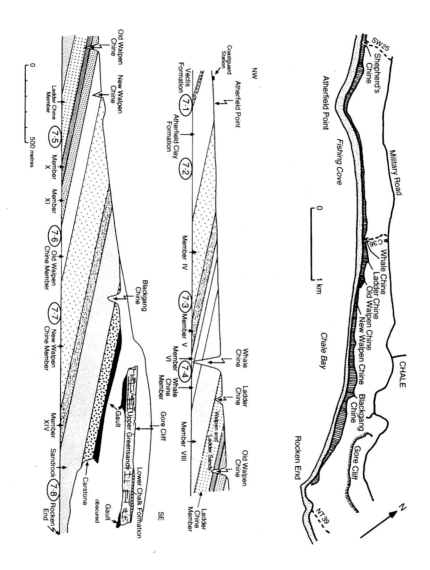

Figure 13. Location map and cliff profile from Atherfield Point to Rocken End.

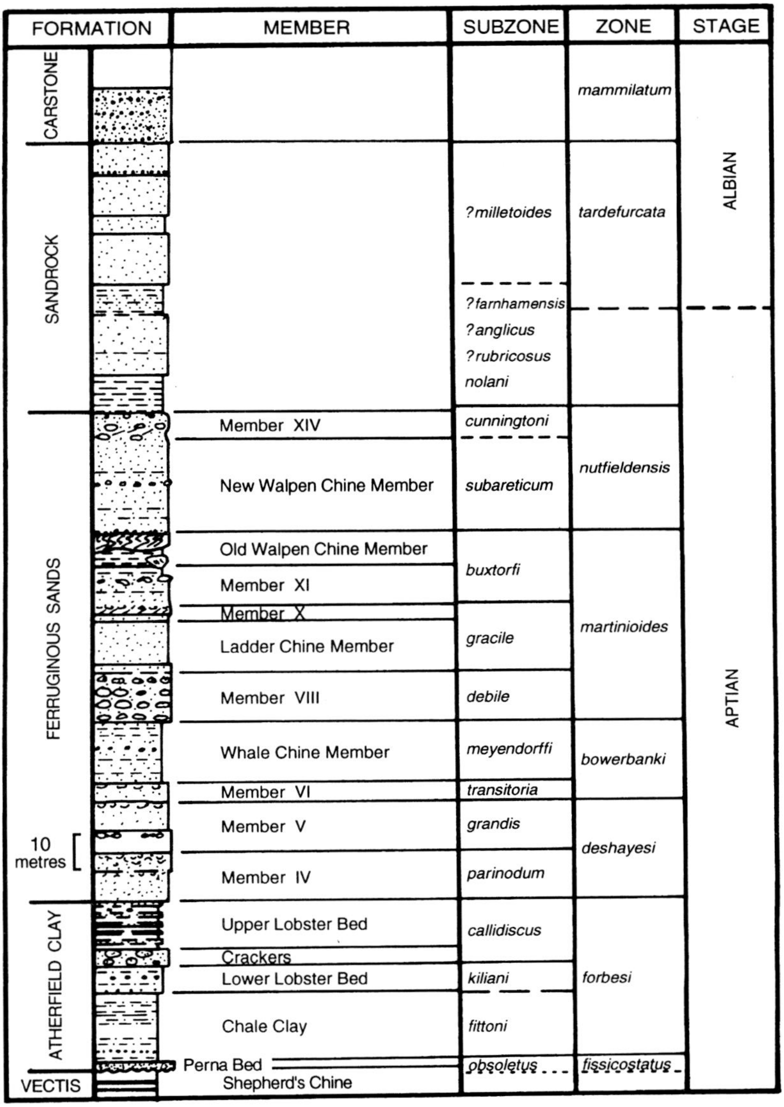

FORMATION		MEMBER	SUBZONE	ZONE	STAGE
CARSTONE				mammilatum	ALBIAN
SANDROCK			?milletoides	tardefurcata	
			?farnhamensis		
			?anglicus		
			?rubricosus		
			nolani		
FERRUGINOUS SANDS		Member XIV	cunningtoni	nutfieldensis	APTIAN
		New Walpen Chine Member	subareticum		
		Old Walpen Chine Member	buxtorfi	martinioides	
		Member XI			
		Member X	gracile		
		Ladder Chine Member			
		Member VIII	debile		
		Whale Chine Member	meyendorffi	bowerbanki	
		Member VI	transitoria		
		Member V	grandis	deshayesi	
		Member IV	parinodum		
ATHERFIELD CLAY		Upper Lobster Bed	callidiscus	forbesi	
		Crackers			
		Lower Lobster Bed	kiliani		
		Chale Clay	fittoni		
		Perna Bed	obsoletus	fissicostatus	
VECTIS		Shepherd's Chine			

10 metres

Figure 14. Stratigraphy of the Lower Greensand Group in Chale Bay.

Chale Bay

Atherfield Point and sometimes as a ledge at low tide on the eastern side of the point. Numerous boulders on the beach provide the best sources of fossils. The contact between the Perna Bed and the underlying dark grey, laminated mudstones of the **Vectis Formation** is a burrowed erosion surface. The Perna Bed comprises five beds. At the base is a thin poorly sorted muddy sand with quartz pebbles, derived fish teeth and bone fragments, phosphatic nodules and rolled Kimmeridgian ammonites. This is the Atherfield Bone-Bed and is a lag developed during the early stages of an important transgression. The remainder of the member consists of four beds of bioturbated grey and green, glauconite-rich, poorly sorted muddy sand. The unit is richly fossiliferous with a diverse fauna which includes bivalves *(Mulletia, Aetostreon, Panopea)*, gastropods, brachiopods, corals *(Holocystis)* and serpulid worm tubes. Trace fossils are abundant, particularly conspicuous being the network of horizontal tunnels connected by vertical shafts, *Thalassinoides,* in bed 3. This member is considered to have been deposited on a shallow marine shelf. The upper three beds are interpreted as firmgrounds resulting from erosion and winnowing during a periods of non-deposition which allowed some cementation to occur. The relatively firm surface created was then colonised by benthic organisms, particularly the large oyster *Aetostreon.*

The **Chale Clay Member** (19 m) consists of mostly unlaminated brown and blue-grey muds with clay-ironstone concretions. This unit is prone to slumping and is usually partly obscured by falls and mudflows. It is sparsely fossiliferous, but the bivalve *Panopea* and echinoids can usually be found. The Chale Clay was deposited in a shallow marine environment intermittently affected by storm events which produced some thin silty lags. It is overlain by the **Lower Lobster Bed Member** (11.6 m), the contact being marked by a resistant ledge at the top of the former. It is darker in colour and slightly coarser than the underlying unit and contains seams of silt and fine sand often with associated gutter casts (sediment-filled linear erosional scours). These seams become more frequent up section towards the overlying Crackers Member. This unit is relatively fossiliferous, yielding the small lobster *Meyerella magna* together with bivalves, gastropods and ammonites *(Deshayesites, Roloboceras)*. The overall upward-coarsening within the member indicates a gradual shallowing and the consequent increasing frequency of storm reworking.

The **Crackers Member** (6 m), two lines of calcareous concretions in a matrix of fine sand, is prominent in the cliff about 500 m east of the Coastguard Station (locality 7.2) and forms a useful marker within the Atherfield Clay sequence. The concretions are large, somewhat irregular in shape and consist of bioturbated silty sand. The lower tier of concretions disappears westwards while, in places, the upper one forms a near continuous bed. Breaks in sedimentation or omission surfaces can be traced from the matrix into the concretions. Associated

Chale Bay

with these omission surfaces are scour-and-fill, fluid escape structures and slumping. The concretions are variable in character. The large ones from the upper layer frequently contain current-aligned monospecific aggregations of *Gervillella* or accumulations of ammonites and gastropods. Some of the smaller nodules have soft cores containing beautifully preserved ammonites, bivalves, gastropods, crustaceans and echinoderms, although a sledge hammer is required to open them. The fossils show little evidence of compaction, suggesting that the concretions were the product of early diagenetic processes. In contrast to the concretions, the sand matrix contains few body fossils.

Above the Crackers, the **Upper Lobster Beds Member** (14.5 m) comprises alternations of muds and sandy silts similar to the Lower Lobster Bed Member. Fossils present are similar to those found in the latter but they are less abundant.

The **Ferruginous Sands Formation** (about 140 m) comprises alternations of muddy sands (usually brown in colour) and dark sandy clays. Eleven subdivisions are recognised in Chale Bay (Figure 14) but they are not all easily distinguishable. The deposits generally lack sedimentary structures, the sands being extensively bioturbated. The succession broadly comprises a number of coarsening-upward units, usually capped by firmgrounds, some of which are discontinuously cemented. The latter results in bands of concretions, which may be calcareous, phosphatic or pyritic and are a major source of fossils within the formation.. The scoured surfaces of the firmgrounds may be overlain either by fossils of firm substrate epifaunal organisms, the large oyster *Aetostreon* being especially common, and/or a lag of derived fossils. Elsewhere body fossils are uncommon. With the exception of the Old Walpen Chine Member, which was deposited in an estuarine environment, the Ferruginous Sands are a shallow marine shelf deposit. The ubiquitous rhythmic units indicate repetitive changes in the rate of sedimentation which may reflect either fluctuations in relative sea-level and/or climate.

The lowest subdivision, the **unnamed Member IV** (7.2 m), is distinguished as a group of bioturbated reddish-brown sandstones. The base is marked by a rapid transition from muddy silt to muddy sand. The sequence contains four coarsening-upward units, each one being capped by a partly cemented firmground. Fossils occur throughout, but tend to be concentrated on the scoured upper surfaces of the firmgrounds, the large oyster *Aetostreon* being particularly conspicuous. At the top of the first firmground, about 3 m above the base of the member, is a 60 cm thick band in which the brachiopods *Sellithyris* and *Sulcirhynchia* occur in so-called "nests" which are interpreted as life assemblages. The top of the member forms a ledge which reaches beach level about 300 m west of Whale Chine (locality 7.3).

The succeeding **unnamed Member V** (14 m) and **Member VI** (about 5.5 m) are difficult to distinguish from each other, both being composed of grey-green, bioturbated, glauconitic muddy sandstones arranged in a sequence of upward-coarsening units capped by firmgrounds. Both units contain discontinuously cemented firmgrounds which appear as irregular lines of concretions. There is a single concretionary band near the middle of Member V, but Member VI contains seven such horizons which form the ledges around the mouth of Whale Chine (locality 7.4). The cemented masses often contain fossils, the most spectacular being the large ammonites *Australiceras, Tropaeum* and *Cheloniceras.*

The **Whale Chine Member** (17 m) forms the bottom of Whale Chine and the lower terrace of the cliff southeast to Ladder Chine. It consists of grey-green muddy sands and sandy clays with concretions. The lower part of the unit is the most fossiliferous, with concretions containing numerous ammonites (*Cheloniceras, Dufrenoyia*), and bivalves (e.g. *Panopea, Thetironia*).

The **unnamed Member VIII** (20 m) forms most of the walls of Whale Chine and the top of the subdivision reaches beach level east of Walpen Chine. It comprises grey to brown muddy sands organised into upward-coarsening units capped by firmgrounds, some of which are discontinuously cemented. These concretionary layers are very conspicuous in the walls of Whale Chine. The concretions contain a black phosphatic core with ammonites (e.g. *Cheloniceras*), bivalves and plant remains. **If time is short or if the tides are inconvenient, this is the best point at which to break the itinerary. The main road can be reached by ascending Whale Chine, but, as indicated earlier, the access via the chine must be checked in advance.**

The **Ladder Chine Member** (20 m) can be recognised from a distance as the homogenous grey sands which form the upper part of Ladder Chine and reach beach level east of Old Walpen Chine (locality 7.5). At the base of the unit is a 0.5 m thick bed of glauconite-rich muds. The sequence, which broadly coarsens upwards, is arranged in upward-coarsening units capped by poorly developed firmgrounds. The large oyster *Aetostreon* commonly occurs resting on these firmgrounds. The large concretions, about 2 m above the base of the member, contains small ammonites (*Epicheloniceras*) or colonies of *Sellithyris* in their brown phosphatic cores. A thin sandstone, about 1.8 m above the concretions, produces a distinct ledge in the cliff. This sandstone contains knots of serpulid tubes. The top of the member is marked by an iron oxide-cemented firmground.

The next unit, the **unnamed Member X** (4 m) consists of reddish-brown muddy sands which form the vertical cliff eastwards from Old Walpen Chine. While this horizon is easily distinguished at a distance, it is more difficult to separate from the underlying unit at beach level. The unit exhibits the usual coarsening-upward units capped with firmgrounds and concretionary bands. It differs from the underlying units by retaining in places some of the original sedimentary structures. Large-scale cross-bedding occurs at several levels and indicates a southeasterly dispersal. Fossils are uncommon except for large *Aetostreon,* which occur in bands in the lower part, and fronds of the fern *Weichselia.* The top of this member is marked by a firmground with abundant branching *Thalassinoides* burrows.

The **unnamed Member XI** (5.5 m) forms lower part of the walls of Old Walpen Chine. It is a bioturbated muddy glauconitic fine sand. In the middle of the unit there are two conspicuous bands of hard ferruginous sandstone with cylindrical branching pyritic *Thalassinoides* burrows. Above these, occasional lenses of cross-bedding occur, the transport direction again being towards the southeast. Apart from plant remains, including leaves of the fern *Weichselia,* body fossils are rare. However, some of the concretions within the *Thalassinoides*-rich bands contain estuarine bivalves.

The next unit, the **Old Walpen Chine Member** (up to 15 m), is easily recognised by its laminated appearance and is clearly visible as the uppermost unit at Old Walpen Chine. It consists of alternations of glauconitic sand and white quartz sand with dark grey mud drapes, with some lenses of cross-bedded sand. Around Old Walpen Chine, the base can be shown to be a major erosion surface, cutting down into the underlying Member XI sands. At the top is a conspicuous band, about 3 m thick, of cross-bedded white quartz sand. This unit is interpreted as an estuarine channel fill. It forms the broad terrace, Walpen Undercliff, between Old Walpen and Blackgang Chines (locality 7.6). The rapid erosion of the Walpen-Blackgang area and the formation of Walpen Undercliff is due to the process of seepage erosion, the springs issuing from within the upper part of the Old Walpen Chine Member (see Itinerary 8).

The relatively thick **New Walpen Chine Member** (about 25 m) forms the vertical cliff backing Walpen Undercliff. It rests on an erosion surface cut into the underlying unit and at the base is a pebble bed containing pebbles of quartzite, limonite, rolled phosphatic nodules and identifiable Upper Jurassic rocks. The lower part consists of bioturbated glauconitic fine to medium sand while the upper part comprises pale, coarse and occasionally cross-bedded quartz sands. Burrows, including *Ophiomorpha,* are common in the upper part. Body fossils are uncommon except near the middle of the division where there is a line of nodules packed with the moulds of rhynchonellids and molluscs, including *Pterotrigonia* and *Thetironia.* This band of nodules is usually accessible in the small embayment about 180 m southeast of Blackgang Chine (locality 7.7).

Blackgang Area

The uppermost division of the Ferruginous Sands Formation, the **unnamed Member XIV** (about 6 m), consists of dark green and brown sands with three bands of ferruginous nodules full of moulds of fossils, notably *Pterotrigonia, Thetironia, Senis, Globularia* and *Anchura*. At the base of the unit is a marker band of very coarse, large-scale cross-bedded ferruginous sandstone with abundant shell debris. As in the lower units, dispersion was towards the southeast. Burrows, including *Ophiomorpha,* occur throughout.

West of Rocken End (locality 7.8), the **Sandrock Formation** (about 70 m) reaches beach level. The base of the formation and its contact with the underlying Ferruginous Sands Formation is usually obscured, but can be seen in the inaccessible cliffs at Blackgang Chine. The base is marked by a conspicuous thick band of black muds. The Sandrock Formation consists of four coarsening-upward units, each one comprising dark glauconitic muds and silts grading up through grey sandy muds and muddy sands into medium to coarse white quartz sands. The sands exhibit a variety of sedimentary structures including large- and small-scale cross-bedding, wavy and flaser bedding. Body fossils are rare but burrows are abundant and include *Ophiomorpha, Thalassinoides* and *Planolites.* The lower part of the sequence can be examined at beach level but the higher parts and the overlying **Carstone Formation** are not easily approachable.

From the beach at Rocken End it is possible to climb across the landslip debris to reach the remnants of the old Niton-Blackgang road either at 492760 or 494759. Alternatively the coastal path passing Knowles Farm (497754) can be taken to reach Niton. The latter part of this itinerary (i.e. the Blackgang Chine to Rocken End section) could be combined with itinerary 5.

8. Mass Movements in the Blackgang Area

The objective of this itinerary is to examine some of the spectacular examples of mass movement which can be seen in the Undercliff, the coastal area between Luccombe in the east and Blackgang Chine in the west. The topography of this area has been formed as a result of an extensive complex of ancient mass movements. Today it forms a tract of land about 0.5 km wide and about 12 km long. Within the zone is a terraced slope beneath a high, often vertical, rear scarp which exposes Lower Chalk Formation and Upper Greensand, both of which are well-jointed. The underlying Gault Clay is an overconsolidated clay and is the layer in which the landslides are "seated". The basal slip surface is usually situated at the top of the lower sandier, non-plastic part of the Gault Clay succession. The landslides are normally of the multiple rotational type and incorporate "slices" of the overlying Upper Greensand and Lower Chalk Formation in back-tilting and seaward translational movements. Below the Gault

Blackgang Area

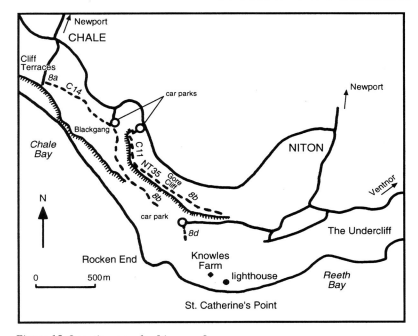

Figure 15. Location map for Itinerary 8.

Clay, the Lower Greensand only becomes an important factor in coastal development at the eastern and western ends of The Undercliff. Seaward of the rear scarp, much of the central Undercliff comprises multiple slides. These are partly masked and fronted by extensive spreads of more broken landslide debris. This material forms relatively smooth or gently undulating surfaces which slope down to the coastal cliffs. These masses have been termed "aprons" (Chandler & Hutchinson, 1982).

The character of The Undercliff landslides has been controlled by the complex interplay of underlying geology, climatic and sea-level changes during the late Pleistocene and Holocene. The available evidence provides a limited history of the mass movements in The Undercliff (Hutchinson, 1991; Hutchinson, Brunsden & Lee, 1991; Hutchinson, Bromhead & Chandler, 1991). During the Devensian it seems probable that large aprons of landslide and solifluction debris were built up on coastal slopes. As sea-level rose during the Flandrian, marine erosion removed parts of these aprons and triggered renewed movements on older slides. It appears that the initial movements took place when sea-level reached about 9 m below O.D. between 7700 and 8500 years ago. Landsliding continued down to about

Blackgang Area

4500 years ago when a period of relative stability set in. A second phase of mass movement began about 4000 years ago and lasted for perhaps 2000 years or more, since when a second phase of relative stability has occurred.

The available data indicate that there are two zones of landslide movement along The Undercliff. Movements in the seaward part of the area involved compound and rotational slides seated in a mud layer close to the base of the Sandrock. Landward of this, movements involved multiple rotational failures on a slip surface within the Gault. Everywhere the landslide scarp faces were degraded by small-scale mass movements, including shallow slides, rock falls and mudslides.

In more recent times, three areas within The Undercliff have been affected by movements, chiefly the renewal of movement of old landslide masses: Blackgang/Rocken End in the west; Luccombe/Dunnose in the east; and Ventnor in the middle. Of these areas, the first two are subject to occasional major movements, while the latter is much reduced in comparison with the other two (Hutchinson, 1965, 1991).

The present excursion visits four separate areas between Chale and St. Catherine's Point which demonstrate different aspects of coastal erosion in an area of strongest marine attack (Figure 15).

References. Bromhead *et al.* (1991), Colenutt (1929), Hutchinson (1987), Hutchinson, Bromhead & Chandler (1991), Hutchinson, Chandler & Bromhead (1981, 1985), Preece (1980, 1986, 1987).

8a. Chale Terrace. Since there is limited parking on the verge close to the entrance to the lane, it is preferable to use the large car park at Blackgang Chine (489768) for this and the succeeding site. Total walking distance, including the return, about 2.5 km from Blackgang Chine.

Walk westwards from the car park along the made road to the point at which footpath C14 is reached. Take this path westwards until it reaches the end of a small lane, Chale Terrace (locality 8a.1). This point overlooks the coast below Blackgang Chine, which is retreating at the rate of about 0.5 m/annum. The stratigraphic sequence exposed in the cliffs below Chale Terrace ranges from the Ferruginous Sands (Member XI) at the base through the Sandrock Formation, with Carstone Formation and Gault at the top close to the chine itself (Figure 16). The cliffs here are undergoing seepage erosion (Figure 17), which takes place above the clay aquacludes within the Ferruginous Sands and Sandrock. At this point, seepage erosion combined with the rock falls that result produce a cliff top retreat rate which is faster than the marine action erodes the base of the cliff. Debris-strewn benches have therefore developed and these are

Blackgang Area

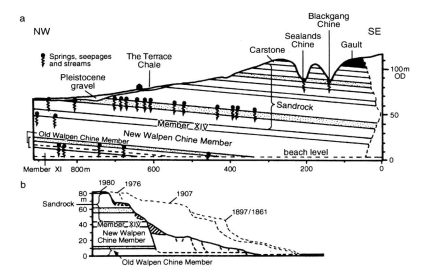

Figure 16.   a. *Cliff profile of the Lower Greensand Group sequence in the Blackgang area (after Hutchinson* et al. *1981).*

   b. *Cross -section of the cliff in the area of Chale Terrace showing inferred slip surfaces and former cliff profiles (after Hutchinson* et al. *1981).*

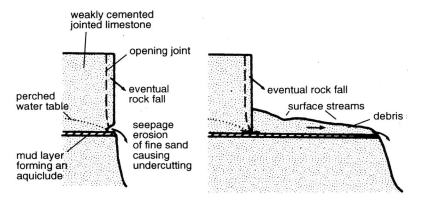

Figure 17. *Diagrammatic sections showing the mechanism of seepage erosion in the Lower Greensand in the Blackgang area (after Hutchinson, 1987).*

well seen from this vantage point. **Do not approach the cliff edge which is very unstable. Return to Blackgang Chine car park.**

8b. Blackgang. Total walking distance about 3 km.

From Blackgang Chine car park, walk eastwards along the old Niton road for about 250 m to the end of the tarmac road, beyond which a rough track continues to the east. This track traverses crosses three of the landslide systems which have been recognised in the area (Figures 18, 19). These systems have a long history of instability, probably in excess of 2000 years, and continue to exhibit intermittent activity.

The tarmac road and track initially crosses the Blackgang Cottage landslide system. Activity in this area probably has a long history, but the best documented movements took place in January, 1994. Following a long period of heavy rainfall, movements took place around the site of Blackgang Cottage. Old deep-seated multiple rotational slides were reactivated and a large elongate mudslide about 60 m wide developed below Blackgang Cottage (Figure 19a). As a consequence of these movements Gore Cliff Cottage and Blackgang Cottage were destroyed, as was part of the former South View access road. The landward side of the system is currently inactive but mudslides, rockfalls, compound slides and rotational landslips continue in the seaward part of the area.

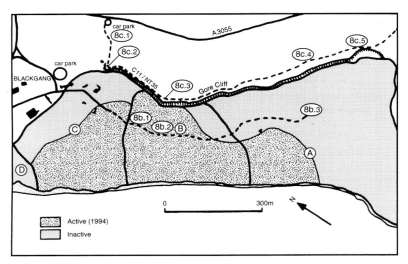

Figure 18. Detailed location map for Itineraries 8b and c, showing landslide systems and active areas (1994): A=South View system; B=Cliff Cottage system; C=Blackgang Cottage system; D=Blackgang Chine-Chale system (modified from Rendel Geotechnics, 1994).

Blackgang Area

The track then enters the Cliff Cottage landslide system. This system has been subject to repeated movements throughout this century (Figure 19a). The area around locality 8b.1 is the site of a mudslide which cut the old Blackgang road in the 1930's. Subsequent movements have taken the form of small rotational landslides at the head of the slide. Further southeast, the path to the area affected by the landslide of March, 1978 (locality 8b.2) which is about 300 m wide. This slide took place after an exceptionally heavy fall of snow, which rapidly melted, followed by a about 10 days of heavy rainfall. This reactivated old landslides, the slip surface being located about 18 m above the base of the Gault (Figure 19b). Below the slip surface the Gault is siltier, mechanically stronger and less plastic, indicating that its position is lithologically controlled and bedding parallel. These movements resulted in the destruction of Sandrock Spring, Sandrock Cottage and Cliff View as well as a section of the old Blackgang road. In January, 1994, this landslide system was reactivated. Activity at this time included the development of deep-seated rotational slides extending back to the rear scarp and the development of a large mudslide about 80 wide to the west of the site of Cliff Cottage (Figure 19a). The Cliff Cottage system is the most active one at present, with extensive mudslides on the seaward side and movements on the deep-seated multiple rotational blocks to landward.

The Upper Greensand is well exposed in Gore Cliff above the coastal path, but is largely inaccessible. However, the transitional beds between the Gault and Upper Greensand can be reached, although with some difficulty, by scrambling across the rubble at the base of the cliff. The lower part of the Upper Greensand is prone to relatively rapid subaerial erosion and this tends to leave the more resistant upper part overhanging. The Upper Greensand is also strongly jointed and consequently small rockfalls are common in this area. The basal part of the Gault, the Carstone and the Sandrock may be accessible below the cliff path, depending on state of the cliff falls. **Great care should be taken in this area, particularly after wet weather, when the cliffs become very unstable.** The Gault outcrop exhibits a series of embayments within which are small mudslides, features typical of stiff, fissured clays.

The track then enters the South View landslide system which is known to have been affected by a number of large-scale movements over the last 200 years. At the end of the path (locality 8b.3) is a view eastwards over a very rugged topography, the result of a succession of landslides (Figure 19a). The oldest dated slide and the largest recorded on the island took place in February, 1799 and involved renewed movements in a complex of old slips. This affected an area some 300 m wide and 600 m from head to toe and cut the original lower Undercliff road. On the far side of the landslipped terrain it is possible to see a small car park which marks the other end of the old upper Undercliff road between Niton and Blackgang which replaced the road destroyed by the 1799 slide.

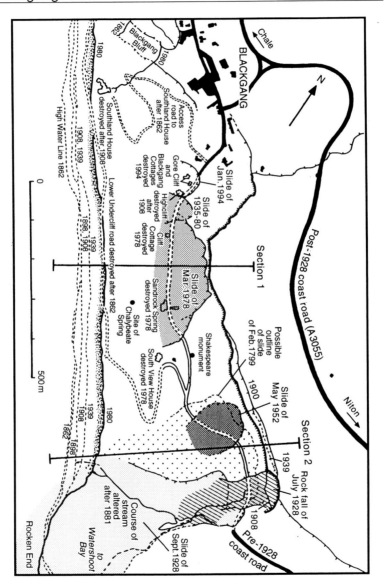

Figure 19. a. Map showing the cliff retreat between 1862 and 1980 and location of the main landslides in the Gore Cliff area (modified from Bromhead et al. 1991).

Blackgang Area

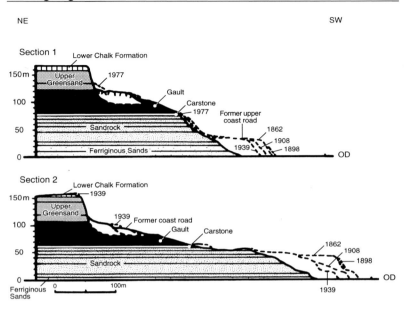

NE   SW

Figure 19. b. Cross-sections 1 and 2 showing retreat of the cliffs between 1862 and 1978 (after Bromhead et al. 1991).

In July, 1928, the largest historically recorded rock fall (toppling failure) occurred with an estimated 100,000 tonnes of rock collapsing from Gore Cliff onto the old road. The great weight of the fall debris appears to have triggered the renewal of movement within old slide debris and, in September, a landslide took place immediately below the rock-fall, carrying away the upper Undercliff road.

While a small slide affected the western side of the area in May, 1952 and several small rock falls have occurred from Gore Cliff, the largest movement in recent years took place in March, 1978 when a major slide destroyed South View House plus a number of chalets and caravans. The South View landslide system has been relatively stable in recent years, activity being largely confined to mudslides and rock falls on the coast and reactivation of the landslide seaward of the site of South View House. **Return along the path to the Blackgang Chine car park.**

8c. Gore Cliff. From Blackgang Chine, drive east along the main road to the viewpoint car park above Blackgang Chine (490767). Parking of coaches

Blackgang Area

here may be difficult at the height of the summer season. The top of Gore Cliff is very exposed and should be avoided in high winds. Total walking distance, including return, about 3 km.

The quarry (locality 8c.1) behind the car park provides an excellent exposure of the top of the Upper Greensand and the base of the Lower Chalk Formation. The **Upper Greensand** comprises shelly sands containing beds of chert nodules. The base of the **Glauconitic Marl** is marked by a thin conglomerate of bored and green-coated reworked Upper Greensand cobbles. The remainder of the Glauconitic Marl (about 1 m thick) is an intensely burrowed calcareous glauconitic sand containing phosphatised fossil fragments, notably ammonites. It passes gradationally up into **Chalk Marl.**

A footpath (C11) can be followed southwards from the car park. About 100 m south of the stile at its beginning, the footpath swings abruptly eastwards (locality 8c.2)(Figure 18a). From this point, on a clear day, there are magnificent views from Blackgang Chine westwards to the Needles and, if conditions are right, the cliffs of Ballard Down and St. Alban's Head on the Dorset coast in the far distance. The cliffs along the southwest coast of the island provide an oblique section through the Brighstone Anticline. Red-tinted Wealden Group sediments form the core of this fold and can be seen beyond Atherfield Point. The reddish-brown sandstones and muds of the Lower Greensand Group can be seen in the foreground dipping gently eastwards in Chale Bay and in the distance dipping westwards in Compton Bay. Beyond the latter point can be seen the white Chalk Group cliffs stretching west, the dip becoming progressively steeper until it is nearly vertical at the Needles. The steeply dipping Chalk Group rocks form the east-west ridge running along the northern skyline. Immediately below this vantage point is the beginning of The Undercliff, an extensive coastal landslip complex that extends eastwards past Ventnor to Luccombe. A number of vegetated back-tilted benches can be seen immediately below the viewpoint. These mark ancient multiple rotational slides.

Continue along the footpath which runs southwards for about 200 m before turning southeast. Below the cliff at this point (locality 8c.3) lies the area affected by the 1935 mudslide and the 1978 landslide (Figure 19a). Some 500 m further southeast (locality 8c.4), the cliff overlooks the area affected by landslides of 1799, 1928 and 1952 (Figure 19a) as well as innumerable small-scale movements. Finally, at the eastern end of Gore Cliff (493760, locality 8c.5), it is possible to overlook the western end of the Undercliff and obtain an idea of the scale of the movements that have taken place over the centuries (Figure 20a). The base of the cliffs consist of Sandrock and the upper part of the underlying Ferruginous Sands. Marine erosion is causing a retreat of about 0.6 m/annum in this area, so that there is constant undermining of the toe of the

Blackgang Area

slips. In contrast, Gore Cliff, which forms the rear scarp of the landslide complex, is relatively stable and is affected only by sporadic rockfalls.

Looking east from the viewpoint, the beginnings of the older mass movements involving large masses of Upper Greensand and Lower Chalk Formation can be seen above St. Catherine's Lighthouse. These stretch from St. Catherine's Point eastwards to Luccombe. There is a marked contrast between the unstable area to the west of the viewpoint and the area to the east which is relatively stable. The most obvious visible difference between the two areas is the presence of wide debris aprons along the base of the landslide complex east of the point. These aprons act both as a toe weighting and as a natural sea wall, increasing the stability of the landslide complex behind them. Notice the conspicuous pair of ridges lying immediately south of the National Trust car park below Gore Cliff. The structure of these ridges can be examined in more detail in Itinerary 8d.

Immediately below the viewpoint, a small deposit of chalky colluvium (hill wash) is exposed on the cliff top. The best exposure is a face about 3 m high at 49327603 (locality 8c.5), which can be approached safely via a convenient ledge. The colluvium consists of a calcareous mud with scattered angular pebbles of chalk, flint and Upper Greensand. The deposit contains about 20 species of terrestrial gastropods, all of which are typically found in calcareous grassland habitats. Palaeontological, archaeological and radiometric dating all indicate that this deposit began to accumulate no earlier than the late 1st or 2nd Century A.D. Since the debris was derived from a northeasterly facing slope which at the time of deposition lay to seaward, the combination of rockfall and landslip must have caused a very significant retreat of the cliff over the last 1800 years. In fact, the currently available evidence suggests that Gore Cliff had more or less its present form by the time that the 1799 landslide occurred. **Return back along the coastal footpath to the viewpoint car park. If on foot, it is possible to reach the starting point of Itinerary 8d by scrambling down the steep slope at the eastern end of Gore Cliff.**

8d. Sandrock Road. From the viewpoint car park at Blackgang, drive eastwards to the National Trust car park at the western end of Sandrock Road, west of Niton (494759). This road is not suitable for coaches. Total walking distance about 1 km.

The upper part of the **Gault,** the **Upper Greensand** and the lowest part of the **Lower Chalk Formation** is well exposed in the vertical cliff northwest of the car park (locality 8d.1). The Gault is a dark blue-grey unfossiliferous silty clay. It passes up transitionally into the Upper Greensand as can be seen at the base of the cliff. The remainder of the sequence is inaccessible but the Chert Beds,

Blackgang Area

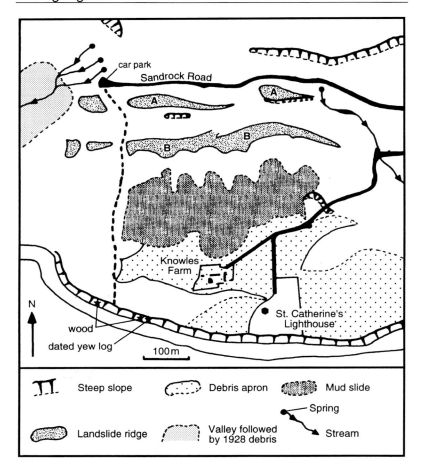

Figure 20. a. Location map for the St. Catherine's Point landslides (Itinerary 8d) (after Hutchinson et al. *1991).*

which are particularly prominent in the upper part of the cliff, can be examined in numerous fallen blocks.

The area below Gore Cliff immediately west of the car park is highly unstable and has been affected by three major slides in historic times (1799, 1928 and 1952; Fig. 19a) as well as numerous smaller scale movements. The car park marks the end of the former coast road from Niton to Blackgang which was

Blackgang Area

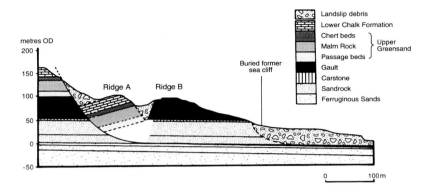

Figure 20. b. Cross-section through the St. Catherine's Point landslides (after Hutchinson, 1987).

carried away in the large-scale slip movements in September, 1928. The car park overlooks the degraded result of all these movements and lies more or less on the boundary between a markedly unstable area to the west and the relatively stable region to the east which has wide debris aprons seaward of the landslide complex.

Sandrock Road lies at the base of a steep debris slope which covers most of the rear scarp of the landslide complex. Take the footpath leading southwards from the car park. Immediately south of the road is a back-tilted block comprising a Lower Chalk Formation, Upper Greensand and Gault succession. This block forms the nearly continuous elongated E-W ridge A (Fig. 20a). At the western end of the ridge, a detached block has foundered westwards towards to valley formed by the 1928 slide. Seaward of ridge A, the footpath crosses a narrow, smooth-floored valley bounded on its southern side by ridge B. The latter consists of Upper Greensand debris, slipped Gault resting on apparently undisturbed, almost horizontal Carstone and Sandrock. Like ridge A, ridge B exhibits detached blocks which have foundered westwards. Recent subsurface investigations (summarised in Fig. 20b) have shown that ridges A and B were not produced by multiple rotational slips. The block including ridge B moved seawards translationally on a basal shear in a clay layer within the Sandrock and overrode the landward edge of the debris apron. This movement may have been promoted by high pore water pressures generated within a perched water table within the Sandrock. As this block slid forward, a graben opened up behind. Ridge A formed subsequently by a rotational slip in the landward face of the graben. Since their formation, the various scarps have degraded. A number of

Cowleaze Chine to Atherfield Point

overgrown mudslide embayments can be seen on the upper part of the seaward slope of ridge B. These are similar to those affecting the lower part of the Gault further west below Gore Cliff. Mudslide lobes, some of which have recently become active again, extend downslope from the embayments to partly cover the extensive debris apron which slopes unevenly down to the coast, the surface being interrupted by compressional ridges and fresh slides.

Subsurface evidence shows that the debris apron rests on a basal slip and buries a 40 m high cliff which forms the seaward edge of the translationally slid block. The available evidence suggests that the buried cliff resulted from the removal of a Pleistocene periglacially generated debris accumulation, accompanied by some erosion of the Sandrock, as sea-levels rose in the during the early Flandrian, perhaps about 8000 years ago. This then triggered a new phase of landsliding, the resulting debris burying the sea cliff and parts of the shore platform. Radiocarbon dates obtained from charcoal and wood found in the debris apron exposed in the sea cliffs west of St. Catherine's Point (locality 8d.2) indicate that this initial phase of movement took place prior to 4500 years ago. There was then a period of relative stability for perhaps a few hundred years until about 4000 years ago when a second major phase of landsliding took place. These two periods of movement produced the thick debris apron. The date of the initiation of the compound slide (translational slide, graben and the rotational slip behind the debris apron) is uncertain, but is considered to have occurred after the Iron Age. **Return to the car park by any convenient route.**

9. Cowleaze Chine to Atherfield Point
The whole of the Vectis Formation and the uppermost part of the Wessex Formation can be examined in an oblique section through the gently dipping southern limb of the Brighstone Anticline exposed on the coast between Cowleaze Chine and Atherfield Point (Figure 21). Rapid erosion has produced marked deterioration of the exposures in recent years, with large parts of the Vectis Formation now obscured by landslips.

Park beside the A3055 about 250 m east of the Atherfield Holiday Camp (451799, parking on the roadside verge only). Take footpath (SW25) to the coast and then follow the coastal path west to Cowleaze Chine, down which the beach may normally be reached. Cliff falls sometimes make access to the area west of Cowleaze Chine possible only at low tide. The cliffs are extremely unstable. Landslides and mudflows are a constant problem along this section. Total walking distance about 5 km.

References. Daley & Stewart (1979), Ruffell (1988), Stewart (1981b), Stewart *et al.* (1991), Wach & Ruffell (1991).

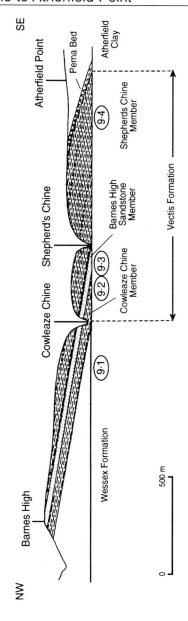

Figure 21. Cliff profile from Barnes High to Atherfield Point.

Cowleaze Chine to Atherfield Point

From Cowleaze Chine walk westwards for about 100 m (locality 9.1). Here the
boundary between the **Vectis and Wessex Formations** is at beach level. It is
marked by an abrupt change from the predominantly red Wessex Formation to
the grey mudstones of the Vectis Formation. Immediately below the contact are
sandstones and sandy mudstones with large mudcracks, soft sediment
deformation structures and cross-bedding, as well as U-shaped and
Ophiomorpha-like burrows. Detailed examination will shows that the
Ophiomorpha-like burrows penetrate downwards from the top of the sandstone
unit. It has been suggested that these trace fossils record a short-lived saline
incursion after the deposition of the sandstone, but this conclusion is now rejected.

The overlying **Cowleaze Chine Member** (8 m) of the Vectis Formation
comprises grey mudstones with a fauna of brackish water bivalves and
ostracods. At the base is a 1 m thick bed of laterally variable, white silty sand,
the "White Rock". The latter is extensively bioturbated and long rootlets
penetrate down from the top of the bed. Near Cowleaze Chine, it contains a
small channel lined with intraformational conglomerate. This bed is considered
to represent a sand flat bordering a lagoon. The remainder of the Cowleaze
Chine Member comprises finely laminated pale silt and grey mud with some thin
bioturbated muddy fine sand beds. It contains a brackish-water ostracod and
mollusc fauna and represents quiet sedimentation in a brackish lagoon.

The Cowleaze Chine Member is overlain by the **Barnes High Sandstone
Member** (about 6 m) which forms a low cliff between Cowleaze Chine and
Shepherd's Chine. The transitional base can be examined immediately east of the
entrance to Cowleaze Chine (locality 9.2). Lenses of silt and very fine sand
appear within the typical Cowleaze Chine finely laminated pale silt and grey
mud lithology. The lenses become larger upwards until true lenticular bedding
appears. The bulk of the Barnes High Sandstone comprises a yellow, limonitic,
upward-coarsening unit, the grain size increasing from very fine or fine sand at
the base to medium sand. At the same time, the sands become better sorted. In
spite of considerable lateral variation, it is possible to demonstrate that there is
also a general upward change in sedimentary structures: wavy and lenticular
bedding, which are common in the lowest part of the unit, are replaced upwards
by small-scale cross-bedding in increasingly thicker sets and this in turn by
large-scale trough cross-bedding. Within the wavy bedded part of the sequence,
mud layers become more widely spaced upwards and finally disappear in the
cross-bedded section. Other sedimentary structures present include various ripple
types (current, wave-current, oscillation, interference and flat-topped), mud
drapes, mud flake conglomerates, reactivation surfaces, herringbone cross-
bedding and small tool marks (brush, groove and prod-marks). The top of the
member is an abandonment surface where sinuous crested mega-ripples occur
with a lag conglomerate of mudclasts and bivalves (*Unio* and *Filosina*) in the

ripple troughs. Various environmental interpretations have been suggested for this sand body including tidal sand flats, barrier bar, lagoonal delta and river mouth bar.

The mudstones of the **Shepherd's Chine Member** (49 m) form the cliffs between Shepherd's Chine and Atherfield Point. The contact with the Barnes High Sandstone can be examined immediately west of the chine (locality 9.3), where it comprises an abrupt lithological change from a limonite-stained conglomerate to a grey laminated mudstone. The Shepherd's Chine Member sequence consists of pale grey siltstones and dark grey mudstones arranged in a number of well-defined, thin (70-90 cm) fining-upward units. About 65 of these laterally continuous units have been recognised in the succession. Each unit usually has a sharp base, sometimes with large scours. Sedimentary structures present include lenticular bedding, parallel lamination, small-scale cross-bedding and gutter casts (straight or sinuous, narrow, sandstone-filled erosional scours). The latter were produced by unidirectional scouring by storm-generated currents and subsequent infilling during waning storm conditions or fair-weather currents. Fronds of the fern *Weichselia,* mostly in the form of fusain (fossil charcoal), occasionally occur in the basal siltstone of some units, particularly in the lowest few metres of the sequence. Fissile mudstones in the upper parts of the units may contain ostracods and poorly preserved bivalves. The origin of the units is uncertain, but they may have been produced by fluvial flood or storm events within a lagoon.

Near Atherfield Point (locality 9.4), the succession becomes difficult to follow due to numerous landslips and associated debris flows. However, it is usually possible to see one or more of the four thin coquina (shell debris) limestones (10-20 cm thick) which occur in this part of the Vectis Formation. Slabs of these are common on the beach.. The limestones are packed with disarticulated valves of the brackish water bivalve *Filosina gregaria.* The base of one of the limestones exhibits numerous small U-shaped *Diplocraterion* burrows. These limestones are considered to have been generated by storms which intermittently swept across the shallow water lagoon. There are also two thin clay ironstone bands about 11 m below the top of the Vectis Formation. The upper one contains the trace fossil *Diplocraterion* and its irregular upper surface is encrusted with oysters. Whilst both fresh- and brackish water faunas occur within the member, greater marine influences are apparent towards the top as indicated by the ostracod faunas and the occurrence of the small elongate oyster *Praexogyra.* At Atherfield Point, the contact with the overlying **Lower Greensand Group** is usually visible (see itinerary 7). **Return to Shepherd's Chine along the beach and ascend the cliff to rejoin the footpath back to the road.**

10. Brighstone Bay

The objective of this itinerary is to examine the cliff and foreshore sections in the Wessex Formation from Chilton Chine eastwards to Ship Ledge (Figure 22). Of particular interest in this area are the large-scale cross-bedded mudstone units and the so-called plant debris beds, of which the Grange Chine Black Band is an excellent example. Coastal erosion is fairly rapid along this part of the coast and the state of the exposures is therefore unpredictable.

The section is accessible either by the footpath (BS72) from the car park at Chilton Chine (410822) or by the footpath (BS57) down the western side of Grange Chine (420817), where there is limited parking on the roadside verge. The cliffs along Brighstone Bay are very unstable. Landslides or mudflows are a constant danger. Large movements can isolate sections of the beach and create a hazard on a rising tide. For this reason the itinerary is best carried out on a falling tide. Total walking distance, including return, about 4 km.

References. Stewart (1981b).

Descend to the beach from the car park at Chilton Chine and walk eastwards. The Chilton Chine Sandstone, a prominent sandstone body within the **Wessex Formation,** descends to beach level immediately east of the chine (locality 10.1). This sandstone thins and becomes finer-grained from west to east. It also exhibits rapid lateral changes when traced eastwards from the chine entrance. It is overlain by a grey mud with abundant carbonised plant debris. Most of the cliff in the neighbourhood of Chilton Chine comprises mainly red-mottled mudstones, but there are some interbedded thin sandstone-mudstone units. Some of these represent crevasse channel fills and crevasse-splay deposits, while others, which contain laterally accreted fining-upward sequences, represent muddy point bars deposited by high sinuosity streams bearing mainly suspended loads. There are also several impersistent grey muds containing carbonised plant debris.

About 500 m east of Chilton Chine (locality 10.2), the Brighstone Sandstone reaches beach level. This is a fining-upward unit formed by point bar accretion in a meandering river carrying a mixed load. It thickens from 2 m in the west to a maximum of 5 m in the east. At the eastern end, the sandstone is cut by an abandoned channel filled with mudstones. 300 to 400 m west of Grange Chine (locality 10.3) is a conspicuous group of interbedded pale green, small-scale cross-bedded, fine-grained sandstones and mudstones exhibiting soft sediment deformation structures. These beds represent a muddy point bar deposit.

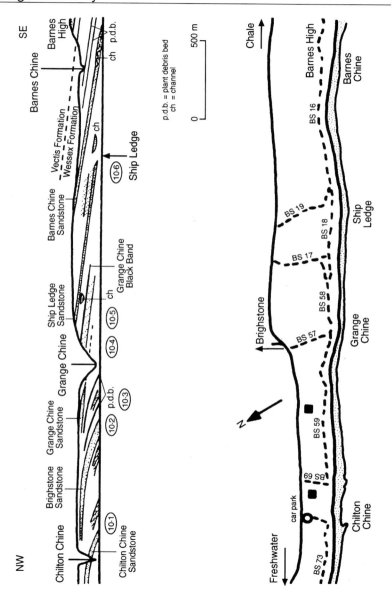

Figure 22. Location map and cliff profile from Chilton Chine to Barnes High (after Stewart, 1981b). p.d.p.=plant debris bed; ch=channel.

Brighstone Bay

Immediately east of Grange Chine (locality 10.4), the conspicuous Grange Chine Black Band can be seen in the cliff. This is a well-developed plant debris bed consisting of grey silty clay with carbonised plant debris, including some large trunks, occasional rolled dinosaur bones, fish and crocodile bone fragments and unionid shells. Much of the plant material is in the form of fusain (fossil charcoal), indicating that local brush fires occurred on the Wealden floodplain. The Grange Chine Black Band dies out eastwards. This and other beds of similar character are interpreted as the results of sheet floods and debris flows (produced by local storms) carrying material into low-lying areas on the alluvial plain, some of which were already occupied by standing bodies of water. Immediately beneath the Grange Chine Black Band is a 3 m thick unit comprising thin, inclined interbeds of very fine-grained sandstone, siltstone and mudstone with, towards the base, a basal 50 cm thick band of sand-sized intraformational mud clasts. This large-scale cross-bedded mudstone unit was deposited by lateral accretion on a muddy point bar and is one of the best examples in the Wessex Formation. The unit also shows various forms of secondary alteration. Most of the unit show vertical striping in purple and red but this stops abruptly at a pale green zone close to the base of the Grange Chine Black Band. The vertical striping was produced by vertical ground water movements in an area with rooted vegetation which allowed oxygen to penetrate differentially into the soil. The zone at the top represents secondary reduction following submergence beneath the ponded anaerobic waters in which the overlying plant debris bed was laid down.

300 m east of Grange Chine (locality 10.5), the Ship Ledge Sandstone appears at the top of the cliff. Between the Grange Chine Black Band and the Ship Ledge Sandstone is a complex sequence of red mudstones with shallow channels with cross-laminated, fine-grained sandstone fills plus some thin, large-scale cross-bedded mudstones.

The Ship Ledge Sandstone is about 1 m thick where it appears at the cliff top and thickens slightly eastwards where it reaches beach level near Ship Ledge (locality 10.6). Unlike many of the sandstones in the Wessex Formation, it has a gradational base and an abrupt top. It is also extensively burrowed. This may represent a crevasse-splay built out into an area of standing water. Immediately above the Ship Ledge Sandstone are further examples of large-scale cross-bedded mudstone units similar to those below the Grange Chine Black Band, although here the primary sedimentary structures are masked to some extent by pervasive colour mottling and vertical stripes. The latter are interpreted as plant root traces.

The area around Ship Ledge provides a good view to the east. The remainder of the Wessex Formation and the Overlying **Vectis Formation** is usually well exposed. The contact between the two formations is marked by a prominent white sandstone which can be seen in the cliff below Barnes High. Also visible is the bright yellow Barnes High Sandstone, the middle member of the Vectis Formation. On a clear day it is possible to see further east to Atherfield Point and Chale Bay. **From this point return to Grange Chine.**

11. Brook Undercliff

The excellent cliff exposures between Chilton Chine and Sudmoor Point (Figure 23) allow a rare opportunity to examine the vertical and lateral relationships within a Wessex Formation fluvial channel sandstone unit, the Sudmoor Point Sandstone, together with the adjacent overbank mudstone deposits.

Although the itinerary can be carried out in either direction, it is recommended that it be made from east to west, commencing at Chilton Chine car park (410822). It is important to note that there are no escape routes from the beach between Chilton and Brook Chines. The cliffs in this area are unstable, with frequent rockfalls, landslides or mudflows. These can isolate sections of the beach and create a hazard on a rising tide. For these reasons it is therefore essential to start the itinerary on a falling tide. Total walking distance about 2 km.

References. Daley & Stewart (1979), Stewart (1981a,b).

From the car park at Chilton Chine, descend to the beach and walk westwards. The Sudmoor Point Sandstone, a very prominent sandstone body within the **Wessex Formation,** is more or less continuously exposed for over 1·5 km along the coast west of the chine. Although appearing to be a single sandstone unit, it is in fact composed of five laterally associated sandstone bodies, each representing a different meander development. These bodies are separated from each other by erosion surfaces representing point bar intersections and can be recognised by changes in the inclination of internal stratification.

At low tide, the Sudmoor Point Sandstone is exposed on the foreshore immediately west of Chilton Chine (locality 11.1). The easterly dipping bedding planes here exhibit ripple marks and occasional dinosaur footprints. A section of a dinosaur trackway from this locality can be seen in the Museum of Isle of Wight Geology at Sandown. From this vantage point, the sandstone can be seen to appear in the cliff about 200 m west of the chine. The internal eastward-inclined beds representing the lateral migration of sloping point-bar surfaces are clearly visible.

About 500 m west of Chilton Chine, the base of the Sudmoor Point Sandstone is

Brook Undercliff

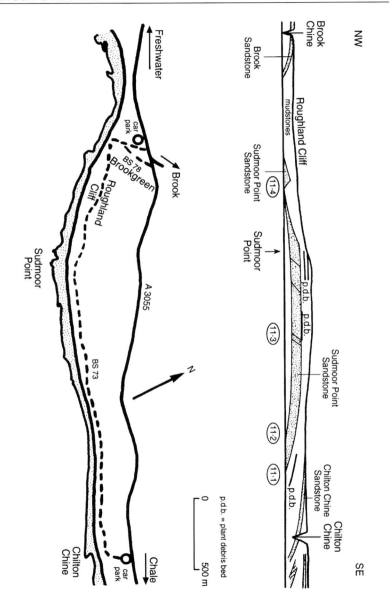

Figure 23. Location map and cliff profile from Chilton Chine to Brook Chine (after Stewart, 1981b). p.d.p. = plant debris bed.

Brook Undercliff

accessible at the bottom of the cliff (locality 11.2). The base is an irregular erosion surface cut into the underlying purple and red colour-mottled mudstone. The lowest part of the unit consists of a conglomerate composed mainly of calcareous intraformational clasts (derived from calcretes formed by pedogenesis in interfluvial floodplain areas), rare extraformational material such as quartz and some rolled dinosaur bones. The conglomerates may be structureless, large-scale trough or planar cross-bedded. The succeeding pebbly sandstones and coarse-grained sandstones are trough or planar cross-bedded below but flat bedded above. Lenses of mud-flake conglomerate occur within these sandstones and associated with the mud-flakes are rare small armoured mud balls. These pass up into fine-grained sandstones with ripple cross-lamination. At the top of this sand body are alternations of fine-grained, flat laminated or small-scale cross-laminated, micaceous sandstones and mudstones. Bioturbation is common in this part of the unit and is also the horizon which yields the dinosaur trackways on the foreshore. Overall, this 6 m thick fining-upward clastic sequence with its associated changes in sedimentary structures is a typical example of a point bar deposit laid down by lateral accretion by a mixed load river.

There is an upward transition into varicoloured and mottled massive mudstones. Fine rootlets may be visible and calcareous nodules, representing the incipient calcrete development, are also present. These mudstones are overbank deposits laid down by vertical accretion of suspended load from ponded flood waters on the alluvial plain adjacent to the river channel. Following deposition, the original laminations were destroyed by bioturbation and pedogenesis (soil formation). Pedogenesis took place in an environment which involved a fluctuating water table and this resulted in the colour mottling and the pseudoanticlines. At times, the rainfall was sufficiently low to allow the development of immature calcrete.

Further west, the composite nature of the Sudmoor Point Sandstone becomes apparent. The most conspicuous major erosion surface can be seen at locality 11.3 (about 1100 m west of Chilton Chine) where two sand bodies can be distinguished by changes in the inclination of internal stratification. Red mudstones visible beneath the sandstone in the cliff and on the foreshore at low tide are overbank deposits.

As Sudmoor Point is approached the sand body thins and becomes finer grained. One of the features of the sandstones in this area is the presence of numerous ball-and-pillow structures at the base of sandstone beds. These consist of lobes and occasionally isolated masses of sandstone surrounded partly or wholly by the underlying mudstone. They were formed by the differential movement of the unconsolidated sand down into the less dense mud below.

At Sudmoor Point (locality 11.4) about 950 m east of Brook Chine, the Sudmoor

Point Sandstone is truncated by a concave-upwards erosional hollow filled with mudstones and subordinate thin sandstones. On the eastern side of the point, the junction between the sandstone and the mudstone represents the erosional bank of the former meander, whilst the inclined sandstones a little further eastwards represent the accretionary bank. This feature therefore represents an abandoned meander channel or oxbow lake subsequently infilled by overbank clays during occasional flood events.

There are few exposures in the broken ground of Roughlands Cliff between Sudmoor Point and Brook Chine. Overbank mudstones can, however, be examined in foreshore exposures at low tide. **The most convenient exit from the section is Brook Chine (384836).**

12. Hanover Point

This itinerary examines the Wealden Group section between Brook Chine and Shippard's Chine (Figure 24), where exposures occur in the northern limb of the Brighstone Anticline. The main interest at this locality is the sedimentology of the Wessex Formation and in particular the plant debris beds, including the so-called "Pine Raft" at Hanover Point, and the several horizons in which dinosaur-induced deformation structures are apparent. Coastal erosion is fairly rapid in this area and the state of the exposures is therefore unpredictable.

Access to the section can be gained either via Brook Chine (384836) or alternatively Shippard's Chine (376842). Ample car parks are available at both. A low tide is essential to see the foreshore exposures, particularly those at Hanover Point itself, and certain points along the traverse cannot be passed at high tide. Total walking distance 4 km, including return to starting point along the beach.

References. Clifford (1936), Ruffell (1988), Scaife (1987), Simpson (1985), Stewart (1981b), Wach & Ruffell (1991), White (1921).

Descend to the beach at Brook Chine (385835) and walk westwards towards Hanover Point. The cliffs of Brook Bay are composed mainly of varicoloured mudstones of the **Wessex Formation** which were laid down as floodplain deposits and subsequently altered by pedogenic (soil-forming) processes. Depending on the state of the exposures, it may be possible to see the Brook Sandstone, which is near the top of the cliff around the entrance to the chine and dips to the east and west, thus marking the position of the hinge zone of the Brighstone Anticline. Grey plant debris beds may also be visible, one directly above and two below this sandstone.

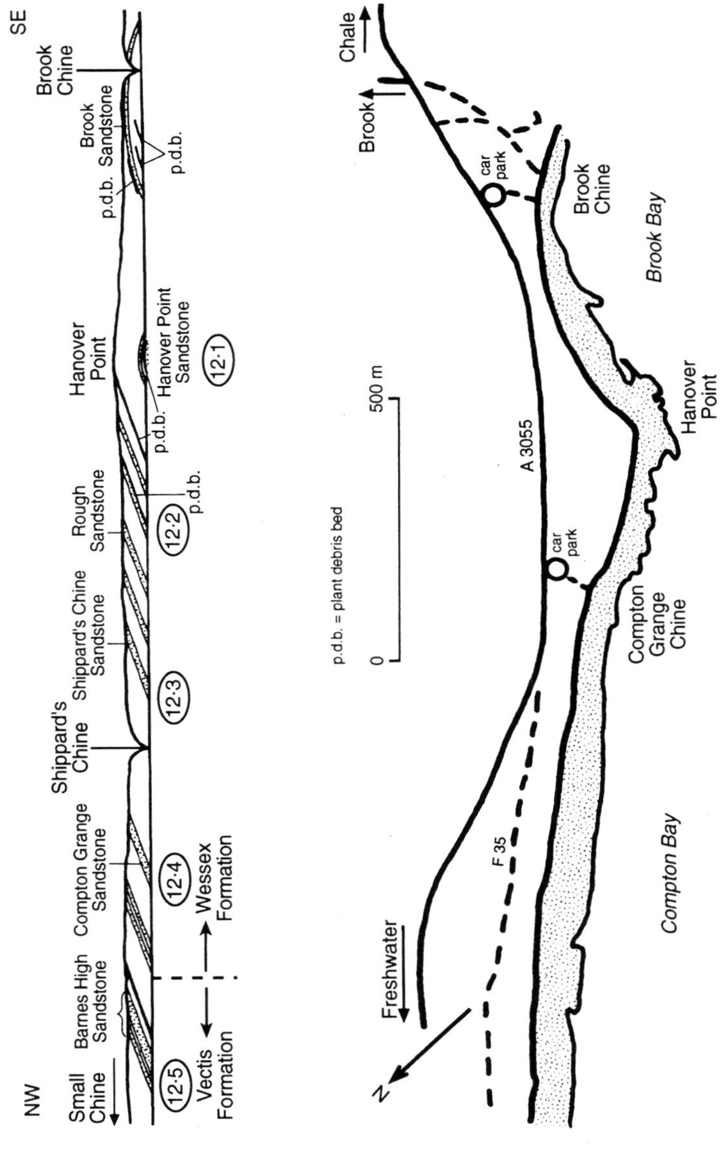

Figure 24. Location map and cliff profile from Brook Chine to Compton Bay (after Stewart, 1981b). p.d.p. = plant debris bed.

Hanover Point

At Hanover Point (locality 12.1), the Hanover Point Sandstone is exposed on the foreshore at low water. At extreme low tide, the underlying Yellow Sandstone may also be exposed. The Hanover Point Sandstone exhibits both small- and large-scale cross-bedding together with some fluid-escape structures and desiccation cracks. The best known feature of this locality is the so-called "Pine Raft". Portions of gymnosperm logs, up to 1 m in diameter and as much as 3 m long, occur scattered over the foreshore exposures but are particularly abundant on the western side of the Hanover Point Sandstone "reef". These logs are derived from the plant debris bed which appears to lie at the same horizon as the Hanover Point Sandstone. Although exposures are always partly obscured by beach debris and seaweed, detailed examination has shown that the fluvial channel in which the Hanover Point Sandstone was deposited eroded the plant debris bed. The plant debris bed is composed of grey muddy silts and fine sands. A search along the outcrop of the plant debris bed can usually reveal logs *in situ*. Some of the logs are carbonised compressions while others are uncompressed carbonate impregnations exhibiting annular rings and other cellular structure. The few preserved *in situ* show a preferred NE/SW alignment.

It is frequently stated that the hinge zone of the Brighstone Anticline is exposed at Hanover Point. Looking at the cliff face from the vantage point of the Hanover Point Sandstone reef, it is easy to see how this conclusion might be reached. However, this is an optical illusion caused by the intersection of northerly dipping Wessex Formation with the change in direction of the coastline at Hanover Point. As noted above, the true location of hinge zone of the Brighstone Anticline lies further to the east, close to Brook Chine.
Northwest of Hanover Point, a sequence dominated by massive red mottled mudstones and pale sandstones with occasional plant debris beds is exposed. Many of the bedding planes on the foreshore on either side of the point show isolated dinosaur footprints and trackways. About 80 m northwest of the point, a conspicuous pale grey sandstone (0.4 - 0.75 m thick) overlain by a grey plant debris bed descends to the base of the cliff. The sandstone has an a very irregular, undulose base and a flat top. Internally the bed shows loading structures and plant rootlet traces extending down from the upper surface. This sandstone bed is the source of the many large boulders which litter the beach. Some of these boulders appear to be large tridactyl (three-toed) dinosaur footprint casts. However, close inspection reveals that they are transmitted prints, that is subsurface layer deformations produced by dinosaur foot impacts.

Some 50 m further northwest, a unit comprising small-scale alternations of fine-grained sand or silt and mud occurs at the base of the cliff. The basal sand infills mudcracks penetrating up to 0.5 m down into the underlying mud. The coarser beds become thinner upwards and the top of the unit grades up into vertically striped and mottled red muds. This unit represents a levee or crevasse-splay deposit. The numerous soft sediment deformation structures within the unit are cross-sections of dinosaur footprints. Immediately above this sequence is a very conspicuous pale sandstone (about 15 cm thick) with rootlet traces. This succession is repeated by a normal fault with a downthrow to the southeast of about 2 m. The fault plane is usually obscured by a mudflow.

About 20 m northwest of the fault, is another unit consisting of interbeds of fine sand or silt and mud. In this case, the coarser beds thicken upwards and at the top there are small sand-filled channels. Burrows and mudcracks occur throughout. This sequence was deposited by a prograding crevasse-splay, the final phase of formation being the erosion and infill of crevasse channels.

About 200 m west of Hanover Point (locality 12.2), a relatively thick grey plant debris bed reaches the base of the cliff. This bed is particularly rich in plant material including gymnosperm logs, stems and cones of the conifer *Pseudofrenelopsis,* and cycad cones. Much of the plant debris in this bed is fusainised, that is in the form of fossil charcoal. It also yields fish and reptile remains. Immediately above the plant debris bed is a complex sandstone body comprising of inclined beds of cross-laminated sandstone alternating with silt or mud. This unit is interpreted as a point bar deposit laid down in a high sinuosity stream bearing a considerable amount of suspended material.

The next unit in the succession is a relatively thick sandstone which forms a prominent ledge crossing the foreshore at low tide. This unit fines upwards from medium- to fine-grained sandstone. The lower part exhibits large-scale trough cross-bedding but above contains small-scale cross-lamination. Viewed from a distance, it can be seen that internally this sandstone body comprises large inclined beds. The fine sand at the top contains distinctive red stripes, probably rootlet traces. A second sandstone body with a similar character occurs some 10 m higher in the sequence. Both these sand bodies were deposited as point bars in high sinuosity streams, the inclined beds representing the original point bar palaeoslopes.

Between the latter sandstone body and the Shippard's Sandstone (see below) are alternations of thin pale silts and thicker red muds. Viewed from a distance, these can be seen to be arranged in large-scale cross-beds. This unit represents a muddy point bar deposited by a stream bearing mainly suspended load. When the exposure is suitable, it may be possible to see that, just before the top of this unit reaches the beach, it is truncated by a steep-sided mud-filled channel. This represents the infill of an abandoned chute or cut-off channel.

60 m southeast of Shippard's Chine (locality 12.3), the 5 m thick Shippard's Sandstone reaches beach level. It is a typical fining-upward fluvial sand body,

which rests on an eroded surface in varicoloured mudstones. Sedimentary structures within the sandstone change from large-scale cross-bedding at the base, through flat bedding and small-scale cross-bedding to interbedded thin sands and muds. This sand body was laid down as a point bar within a meandering stream channel.

The area around Shippard's Chine is currently undergoing rapid erosion and exposures are consequently rather poor. The conspicuous large-scale cross-bedded Compton Grange Sandstone reaches the base of the cliff about 75 m west of the chine (locality 12.4). This 3 m thick sand grades upward from very coarse or coarse to medium sand and contains some pink quartz grains. It is overlain by a plant debris bed containing pyritised wood. Towards the top of the Wessex Formation are two cross-bedded sandstone units, the upper one containing *Ophiomorpha*-like burrows similar to those seen at the equivalent level near Cowleaze Chine (Itinerary 9).

The **Vectis Formation** (66.5 m), as elsewhere, can be divided into three members. The **Cowleaze Chine Member** (about 7 m) consists of rhythmic units comprising bioturbated pale siltstones and dark grey laminated or massive mudstones containing a shelly fauna of *Viviparus, Filosina, Unio* and ostracods. At the base is a pale grey, coarsening-upward silty sandstone which resembles, and is probably the lateral equivalent of, the "White Rock" at Cowleaze Chine and like it was deposited as a sand flat bordering a lagoon. Several thinner siltstone/fine sandstone beds occur higher up in the unit. The major part of this member was deposited in a shallow brackish lagoon.

The **Barnes High Sandstone Member** reaches beach level about 300 m west of Shippard's Chine (locality 12.5). Here, it is represented by three coarse sandstone beds separated by grey mudstones. Each of these sandstones coarsens upwards from an abrupt or gradational base and has an abrupt top. All three contain large-scale cross-bedding, wavy and lenticular bedding being uncommon. The central sand body is 4 m thick, has a gradational base, exhibits lateral accretion structures and has bivalve casts in its uppermost 3 cm. The depositional environment of the Barnes High Sandstone here is uncertain, but the current interpretation indicates that it was laid down during separate progradational phases of a lagoonal delta.

The overlying **Shepherd's Chine Member** is not well exposed here. Isolated exposures show that it comprises a number of fining-upward units from pale silt or fine sand to dark grey mud. A thin (10-15 cm thick) very coarse, iron-cemented sandstone occurs about 10 m above the base of the member. Thin coquina limestones (up to 15 cm thick) occur in the upper part and blocks of these are common on the beach. This member was deposited in a shallow

Compton Bay

brackish lagoon, the coquina limestones being generated by intermittent storm events.

West of Small Chine, the upper 60 m of the Wessex Formation and the lowest 27.5 m of the Vectis Formation are repeated by a normal fault with a downthrow to the southeast of about 43 m. The absence of the upper part of the Vectis Formation may indicate rapid thinning within a very short distance or the presence of a second fault but since this area is very badly exposed as a result of landslips, this is currently unresolvable. It seems likely, however, that there is a second fault west of the known one, which cuts out the upper part of the repeated Vectis Formation sequence.

Return to Brook Chine along the beach, unless there is an adverse tide when the beach should be exited via Shippard's Chine.

At intervals between Brook Chine and Shippard's Chine, the cliff top is capped by a prominent bed of fluvially deposited gravel resting unconformably on the Wealden Group sediments. The basal part of this gravel is sandier and contains plant material including logs, twigs and fruits of alder (*Alnus*) and hazel (*Corylus*). This is consistent with a wet woodland which was presumably developed along a river valley floor. The bed also yields occasional late Mesolithic artefacts and Mesolithic hearths have been seen in the past. Pollen data indicates that this bed was deposited during the Flandrian (zone II), about 6500 years ago. The bed is easily accessible at the side of the path at Shippard's Chine.

13. Compton Bay
This itinerary covers the Cretaceous sequence exposed in an oblique section through the northern limb of the Brighstone Anticline in Compton Bay. It extends from the base of the Lower Greensand Group to the lower part of the White Chalk Formation.

The Upper Greensand to Chalk cliff section can only be approached at moderately low tides and particular care should be taken avoid being cut off by a rising tide. The walk commences at the car park a short distance above Compton Chine (370851, Figure 25). The car park is not suitable for coaches. The cliffs are vertical or even, in places, overhanging and a hard hat should always be worn here. Avoid the section completely after frost or heavy rain, when there is a constant rain of debris, or when there is a strong south to west wind blowing. Total walking distance about 4 km, including rough walking and scrambling over seaweed covered boulders along much of the section.

Compton Bay

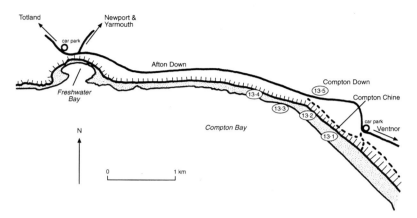

Figure 25. Location map for Itineraries 13 and 14.

References. Dike (1972b), Jefferies (1963), Kennedy (1969), Owen (1971), Wach & Ruffell (1991).

From the car park, cross the main road and follow the coastal footpath eastwards for about 100 m. From this point it is possible to descend to the beach. **It is no longer possible to reach the beach via Compton Chine.** The **Lower Greensand Group** (Figure 26) is exposed in the cliffs immediately to the west. The Vectis Formation/Lower Greensand Group contact is not visible in the cliff where it is obscured by landslips. It can sometimes be found on the foreshore, particularly if a recent storm has removed the shingle. Much of the **Atherfield Clay Formation** (about 25 m), including the **Perna Bed,** is hidden by slips and vegetation.

The **Ferruginous Sands Formation** (about 50 m) is much thinner here than in Chale Bay (Itinerary 7) and the subdivisions seen at the latter locality are not easily recognisable. Much of this formation east of Compton Chine consists of deeply weathered, unfossiliferous red-brown sandstones with considerable numbers of irregular ironstone bands. West of the chine (locality 13.1), the upper part of the Ferruginous Sands Formation shows more variability with beds of bioturbated and/or cross-bedded glauconitic sandstones, sandy mudstones and thin conglomerates.

The base of the **Sandrock Formation** (about 25 m) is marked by a conspicuous thick band of black bioturbated, glauconitic muds. The formation consists of two coarsening-upward units, each comprising dark glauconitic muds and silts

Compton Bay

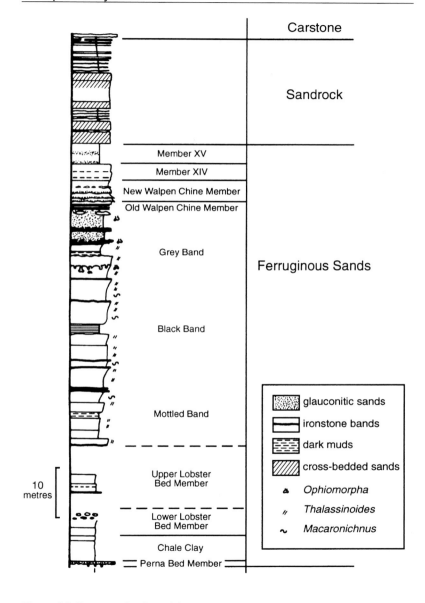

Figure 26. Stratigraphic log of the Lower Greensand Group, Compton Bay (after Wach & Ruffell, 1991).

grading up through grey sandy muds and muddy sands into medium to coarse white quartz sands. The sands exhibit a variety of sedimentary structures including large- and small-scale cross-bedding, wavy and flaser bedding. A variety of trace fossils is also present including *Ophiomorpha, Teichichnus* and *Thalassinoides,* but body fossils are absent. At the top of the unit is a glauconitic black mud, probably the eroded remnant of a further coarsening-upward unit.

The **Carstone Formation** (2 m) rests on an irregular erosion surface cut into the Sandrock. It comprises a reddish-brown bioturbated medium to coarse sandstone with a basal conglomerate of quartz pebbles.

The **Gault Clay** (about 30 m) outcrop is clearly marked by the cliff re-entrant (locality 13.2). As usual on the Isle of Wight, it consists of a dark grey mud. Fossils are scarce but the ammonite *Hoplites* and the bivalves *Inoceramus sulcatus, Lima parallela* and *Panopea gurgitis* may be found occasionally. Much of the central part of the Gault sequence is obscured by vegetation and slips. West of the Gault re-entrant, the transitional beds between the Gault and the Upper Greensand can usually be examined. These consist of bioturbated buff silt and dark grey silty muds.

The **Upper Greensand** proper consists of buff and pale grey-green silts and fine sandstones with bands of calcareous and, in the upper part, siliceous concretions, together with scattered dark brown phosphatic nodules. The weathered surfaces frequently yield tubes of the serpulid worm *Rotularia concava* and the bivalve *Exogyra obliquata.* The uppermost 2 m of buff glauconitic marls contain bands of phosphatic nodules which have yielded rare ammonites of the uppermost Albian zone of *Stoliczkaia dispar.* **The highest part of the Upper Greensand forms a small headland which is a critical cut-off point. It should only be passed on a falling tide and a return be made at least three hours before the following high tide.**

The **Lower Chalk Formation,** dipping northwards at about 45°, is well exposed in the cliffs and narrow foreshore exposures about 600 m west-northwest of Compton Chine. The erosive contact between the Upper Greensand and the base of the **Glauconitic Marl** is generally well exposed just west of the small headland (locality 13.3). The contact shows dark green glauconitic sand piped down into the Upper Greensand within *Thalassinoides* burrows. Immediately above the contact is a basal conglomerate comprising cobbles of reworked Upper Greensand and phosphatic nodules. The remainder of the Glauconitic Marl is a dark green, intensely bioturbated, glauconitic sandstone about 4 m thick. Fossil are abundant and including ammonites (*Schloenbachia, Mantelliceras*), bivalves (*Pycnodonte, Chlamys*), serpulids and sponges, *Exanthesis labrosus* being especially common.

Compton Bay

The **Chalk Marl** comprises alternations of grey marls and white limestones. The lower part of this sequence is condensed at this locality and contains several levels of phosphatic nodules in a coarse glauconitic matrix. Much of the sequence is intensely bioturbated and pyrite nodules are common. A rich fossil fauna is present including ammonites (*Schloenbachia, Mantelliceras, Acanthoceras*), bivalves (*Inoceramus, Pycnodonte*), brachiopods, echinoids (*Holaster*), serpulids and sponges. About 18 m above the base, there is a marked lithological change, interbedded limestones and marls being replaced by grey to white limestones with minor grey marl seams, the **Grey Chalk**. The marls in the beds immediately below the change contain abundant specimens of the small brachiopod *Orbirhynchia mantelliana*. Approximately 7 m above the base of the Grey Chalk, is a massive hard chalk unit (called Jukes-Browne Bed VII)with coarse, laminated lenses containing examples of the large ammonite *Acanthoceras jukesbrownei*. At the junction between the Grey Marl and the overlying **Plenus Marls Member** and about 10 m below it are prominent burrowed erosion surfaces. The marl flasers and modified burrows, which are common in the Chalk Marl and Grey Chalk, are the result of post-depositional compaction. The Plenus Marls is a distinctive unit comprising about 4 m of blue-grey marls and pale grey limestones. **This horizon and the White Chalk Formation succession further west are only accessible at low tide.**

The base of the White Chalk Formation is marked by the nodular chalks of the lower **Ranscombe Member** which contain small white chalk pebbles, uncoiled (straight) ammonites (*Sciponoceras* sp.) and the bivalve *Inoceramus*. The central part of the Ranscombe Member is nodular with many chalk pebbles. Whole and fragmentary shells of the inoceramid bivalve *Mytiloides mytiloides* are abundant at this level, and small fossils, including bryozoa, brachiopods and echinoids, can be collected from air-weathered surfaces. One bed contains abundant fragments and occasional whole calyces of the free-swimming microcrinoid *Roveacrinus*. The highest part of the Ranscombe Member comprises uniformly thick beds of smooth white chalk separated by thin marls.

The base of the **St. Margaret's Member** (Spurious Chalk Rock of Rowe) descends to sea-level about 350 m west of the small headland formed by the top of the Upper Greensand (locality 13.4) and can be examined both *in situ* and in fallen blocks. At the base of this member is the Ogbourne Hardground. This is a massively lithified 30 cm thick chalk bed, stained orange-brown by iron oxides and whose upper surface is coated with green glauconite. The upper part of this bed contains *Thalassinoides* burrows several centimetres in diameter, which were constructed before lithification took place, together with the complex borings made by sponges in the hardground surface. The Ogbourne Hardground marks a major local break in sedimentation which is represented in Sussex and Kent by 30 to 40 m of soft white chalk.

Freshwater Bay

No attempt should be made to continue beyond this point into Freshwater Bay. Return along the beach to the access point.

If time permits, it is worth walking up the coastal footpath to the A3055 road cutting on Compton Down (locality 13.5). The section here provides access to higher parts of the sequence that cannot be safely reached in the cliff section below. **Care should be exercised here since the verge is narrow and the road can be very busy in summer.** At the eastern end of the cutting, the Ogbourne Hardground at the base of the St. Margaret's Member is visible just above the scree. 3·5 m above the top of the hardground lies the "Black Band", a thin marl correlatable with the Southerham Marl in Sussex. 4·5 m above this is a bed rich in the bryozoan *Bicavea.*

14. Freshwater Bay

Freshwater Bay affords easily accessible sections through highly tectonised chalk in the Chalk Formation which was in places broken up by freeze-thaw activity under periglacial conditions during the Pleistocene.

Vehicles (other than coaches) may be parked either in the car park in the centre of the bay or in that immediately west of the Albion Hotel (Figure 25). Coaches may be parked in a small car park above the eastern side of the bay. While parts of the section are accessible at most states of the tide, a mid- to low tide is preferable.

At low tide, the western side of the bay provides exposures of steeply dipping beds within the middle of the, **White Chalk Formation,** including the upper part of the **St. Margaret's Member** and the lower part of the **Broadstairs Member.** The paired Navigation Marls, 40 cm apart, can be seen in the landward side of the cave roof at low tide level. The single 5 cm thick East Cliff Marl occurs 20 cm higher up the sequence. On either side of the metal stairway leading into the cliff, well-bedded weakly nodular chalks contain thin wispy marl partings and abundant flint nodule bands. The chalk in this part of the succession contains many fragments of the bivalve *Inoceramus.* Many of the flints are full of small cavities. The highest marl parting can be found at the recess just north of the stairs. The overlying white chalks contain bands of flint nodules and tabular flint sheets, although these are considerably fractured. **Do not be tempted to pass through the caves at very low tide into Watcombe Bay since it is very easy to get trapped by the tide in this area.**

The middle part of the Chalk Formation is also exposed on the eastern side of the bay, but here it has been extensively disturbed by freeze-thaw activity and is overlain by Quaternary deposits which partly infill a north-south palaeovalley.

Alum Bay

Near the centre of the bay, the base of the succession is formed of a conglomerate comprising rolled flints, together with some chert and ironstone. This is a fluvial gravel of unknown, but presumably early Devensian, date. It is overlain by a crudely bedded chalk rubble (**Coombe Rock**) which thickens towards the centre of the bay where it is up to 2 m thick. Throughout most of the eastern side of the bay, this deposit overlies and grades down into the greatly disturbed White Chalk Formation bedrock. The Coombe Rock was formed by a combination of bedrock break-up resulting from intense freeze-thaw activity and gelifluction, the downslope movement of water-saturated debris over the frozen subsurface. It has yielded teeth of the mammoth, *Mammuthus primigenius,* indicating a Devensian age. Near the centre of the bay, the Coombe Rock is overlain by a bedded flint gravel. This is another fluvial deposit, presumably of late Devensian age.

15. Alum Bay

The famous "coloured sands" make Alum Bay the best known and most visited geological locality on the Isle of Wight (Figure 27). With their continuation into Headon Hill (see itinerary 16), the cliffs of Alum Bay exhibit an essentially complete sequence from the uppermost part of the Chalk Group through the late Palaeocene to late Eocene beds. The subject of serious study since the nineteenth century, the Alum Bay and Headon Hill Palaeogene sequence together represent one of the most stratigraphically extensive Tertiary successions in western Europe. From the Reading Formation exposures at the southern end of the bay northwards to where the Becton Sand occurs to the north of Alum Bay Chine, ten Palaeogene formations comprising in excess of 400 m of strata represent some 15 million years of geological time (Figure 28). This sequence reflects a variety of depositional environments; shallow marine shelf, littoral, lagoonal, marsh and fluvial conditions are all represented. In general, the sequence is not richly fossiliferous, but animal and plant fossils are common at certain horizons. It is the custom to refer to various stratal groupings within the Alum Bay by the "bed" numbers used by Prestwich (1846), who provided the first detailed account of the stratigraphy here.

Vehicles may be parked in the car parks at the Needles Pleasure Park (306854). From the car parks, the beach can be reached either by the steps down Alum Bay Chine or, in the holiday season, by the chair lift. Most of the section can be reached at any time except at high water spring tides or during severe gales. Depending on the state of the mudflows at the southern end of Alum Bay, the Chalk may not be accessible at normal high tide. The cliffs are vertical or even, in places, overhanging and a hard hat should always be worn here. It is not advisable to work beneath the cliffs either after frost or heavy rain, when there is a constant rain of debris, sometimes quite large. It should be noted that Alum Bay is a very popular tourist

Alum Bay

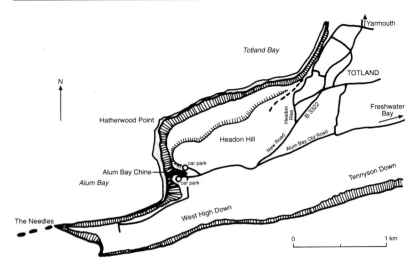

Figure 27. Location map for Itineraries 13 and 14.

attraction and the car parks and beach may very crowded at the height of
the summer season. **Total walking distance about 1·5 km.**

References. Buurman (1980), Crane (1977), Daley & Edwards (1974), Eaton
(1976), King (1981), Plint (1983), Prestwich (1846), Rowe (1908), Stinton
(1971), White (1921).

Before descending to the beach from the cliff-top, one can gain a very fine view
of the Needles, a distinctive line of three sea stacks forming the western tip of
the Island. Early 17th century charts show a cluster of 14 narrow columns of
Chalk (now eroded away) to the north of the present Needles, which must have
given the feature its name. A tall stack, known as Cleopatra's Needle or Lot's
Wife, once stood between the first and second Needles, but fell in 1764. The
Needles owe their existence to a particularly hard zone within the White Chalk
Formation caused by greater tectonic compaction locally.

Descend to the beach and walk to the southernmost corner of the bay. From
here, the general arrangement of the sequence can be seen (Figure 28). The
Chalk Group and the whole of the Palaeogene sequence south of Alum Bay
Chine have a vertical dip and a nearly east-west strike. This section is eroded
through the northern limb of the Brighstone Anticline. Northwards, beyond
Alum Bay Chine, the dip changes rapidly from vertical to near-horizontal.

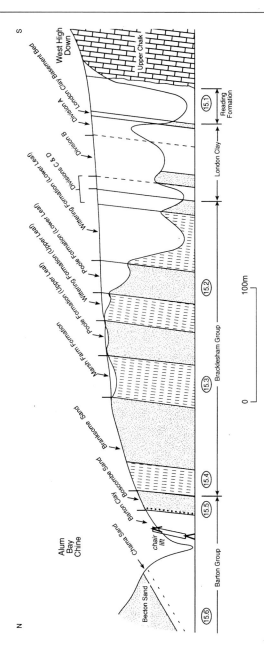

Figure 28. Cliff profile of the Palaeogene section in Alum Bay.

Alum Bay

The **White Chalk Formation** in Alum Bay dips at about 80°N and is the highest Campanian Chalk present in the island. It can be examined at low tide at the base of the cliff and in fallen blocks. **Do not attempt to walk or wade along the base of the cliffs to the Needles since the tidal race between Scratchell's Bay (to the south) and Alum Bay can be fast and dangerous.**

The contact between the **Studland** and **Portsdown Members** can be found by walking about 50 m along the base of the cliff from the Palaeogene erosion surface. The junction is marked by a change from hard, thinly-bedded limestones with thin wispy marls (Portsdown Member) to softer, marl-free beds with regularly spaced beds of large nodular flints (Studland Member). Fallen blocks of the Portsdown Member contain numerous examples of the small, pointed echinoid *Echinocorys subconicula.* The Studland Member contains a richer fauna, commonly including the small brachiopod *Magas chitoniformis,* diverse oysters and starfish ossicles. The zonal belemnite *Belemnitella mucronata* can also usually be found. Large vertically-oriented barrel- and pear-shaped flints, called potstones, are common in the uppermost few metres of the Chalk. Several project out of the cliff face, while others lie scattered on the beach. Each of these flints formed around a vertical burrow.

The junction between the Chalk Group and the **Reading Formation** (25·6 m) is usually visible at the southernmost corner of the bay (locality 15.1). The surface beneath the unconformity contains large hollows (up to 2 m in diameter) which penetrate several metres into the underlying White Chalk Formation. These formed as solution hollows on a subaerial surface prior to the deposition of the Reading Formation.

At the base of the Reading Formation is a thin brown sand, which lies on and infills the irregularities in the underlying White Chalk Formation. These sands are about 15 million years younger than the White Chalk immediately below, the contact representing a period of erosion (including the formation of solution hollows) and non-deposition. Immediately overlying the junction are pockets of rolled and unrolled flints. The remainder of the Reading Formation is usually poorly exposed, being covered by a spectacular mudflow. A section may be visible at the top of the Reading Formation gully, but this may be difficult to reach unless the mudflow is reasonably dry. The sequence consists of red, brown, grey and purple massive muds, striped or colour mottled in places. Such features are considered to have been produced by soil forming processes shortly after deposition and reflect fluctuations in the water table due to a markedly seasonal rainfall in a warm climate.

The next formation, the **London Clay** (about 70 m) is taken here to include all the strata from the top of the Reading Formation up to and including Prestwich

Alum Bay

Bed 6. It should be noted that the stratigraphic location of the top and bottom of this formation is placed elsewhere in some other accounts of the locality. The London Clay is normally well exposed. Calcareous fossils (mainly gastropods and bivalves) are generally well-preserved except in the upper part of the unit where leaching has left only moulds.

The contact of the London Clay with the Reading Formation is only occasionally visible, but may be located by shallow digging on the northern edge of the Reading Formation gully. It is a burrowed erosion surface, some of the burrows being preserved as ironstone casts. Four subdivisions can be recognised within the London Clay sequence. The lowest subdivision, the **London Clay Basement Bed** (Oldhaven Formation of King, 1981), comprises 4·3 m of glauconitic sandy silts with shelly lenses. At the very base is a discontinuous, patchily lithified pebbly sand, the pebbles being well-rounded and consisting of Reading Formation mud, chalk and flint. The succeeding subdivisions consists of three coarsening-upward units. **Cycle 1** (16 m) begins with silty and sandy muds with *Astarte*. These pass up into silts with common *Pholadomya* and *Ditrupa,* followed by sandy silts with abundant double valves of *Panopea* in life position and a diverse fauna including *"Corbula", Turritella,* etc. In the uppermost part of the cycle black flint pebbles occur. **Cycle 2** (38 m) comprises silty muds, sometimes glauconitic, passing up into interbedded fine sands and muds. Discontinuous calcareous concretionary bands are particularly conspicuous at this level. Shell seams and lenses in the lower part yield *Pinna, Arctica* and *Turritella.* About 15 m above the base is a partly cemented shell bed with *Venericor.* **Cycle 3** (11 m) is composed of sandy silts, with a flint pebble bed at the base, overlain by glauconitic laminated fine sands. The sandy silts contain numerous clay ironstone nodules. Moulds of molluscs such as *Glycymeris, Pitar* and *Turritella* are common. The sands at the top of Cycle 3 are currently assigned to the overlying Bracklesham Group.

The London Clay is clearly a marine deposit. Each cycle indicates a similar pattern of events; the finer sediments at the base of the cycle represent low energy shelf deposition following a marine transgression, whilst the slightly coarser upper part reflect a subsequent shallowing.

The cliffs in the central part of the bay expose the most prominent lithological unit, the **Bracklesham Group** (about 230 m). The precise relationships of this part of the succession with lateral equivalents elsewhere in the Hampshire Basin have until recently been uncertain and hence it has been referred to as the "Alum Bay Sands" (Daley & Insole, 1984). It is now possible to recognise four separate formations, although the situation is complicated by the interdigitation of two lower formations. As a whole, the Bracklesham Group consists of sand bodies which alternate with heterolithic units consisting of finely interbedded muds,

Alum Bay

silts and sands. It is from the sand bodies within this part of the succession that most of the famous "coloured sands" derive. Although about 20 colours are recognisable, they reflect mixtures of grains of six main colours: white, yellow, brown, red, green and black. All the sands are predominantly composed of quartz. White sands are formed of quartz grains with no mineral staining or grains of other material. Green sands are due to the presence of grains of the green potassium-iron-alumino-silicate mineral glauconite. Glauconite is an unstable mineral when exposed to weathering, its decomposition producing various iron oxides. These impart various shades of red, brown and yellow depending on the concentration and composition of the iron oxides involved; hematite gives a red colour, while limonite produces browns and yellow. Finally, a black colour is caused by the inclusion in the sand of small particles of carbon (derived from plant material). The heterolithic units which alternate with the sands are grey to brown in colour and contain a variety of sedimentary structures including small-scale cross-bedding, lenticular and flaser bedding. Fossils are not common within the Bracklesham Group, but plant remains (including leaves and rootlets) and burrows occur at some horizons.

The lowest unit in the Bracklesham Group sequence is the first occurrence of the **Wittering Formation** (Prestwich Beds 7-13; approximately 45 m). This is a predominantly heterolithic unit and exhibits a variety of sedimentary structures including lenticular and flaser bedding. Some sands occur within the sequence and these may have a channel-like form and may be cross-bedded.

The first occurrence of the Wittering Formation is followed by the lowest appearance of the **Poole Formation** (Prestwich Beds 14-18; 23 m). This is a sand unit, exhibiting ripple lamination and cross-bedding and containing flint pebble beds overlying scoured surfaces. About 7 m above the base of the formation (locality 15.2) is the Alum Bay Leaf Bed (1.2 m), a very fine white to cream clay of a type formerly termed a "pipe clay" and a thin lateral equivalent of the "Ball Clay" extracted commercially further west in Dorset. Unfortunately leaf impressions are less common than they once were, but a few specimens can usually be found if time is spent splitting the finely laminated clay. The leaves are mainly "entire-margined" (i.e. untoothed) and this suggests a tropical or warm climate. A prominent, hard ironstone band occurs a few metres below the leaf bed.

The base of the second occurrence of the **Wittering Formation** (Prestwich Beds 19-20; 23 m) is marked by sandy muds with *in situ* rootlets. This is the local equivalent of the Whitecliff Bay Bed (see Itinerary 2). The remainder of the formation is predominantly heterolithic. A second occurrence of rootlets occurs at the top of the unit. The second development of the **Poole Formation** (Prestwich Beds 21-23; about 25 m) comprises sands, mainly cross-bedded, together with pebbly lenses and bands. *Ophiomorpha* burrows occur in the lower part of the unit.

The succeeding, very distinctive **Marsh Farm Formation** (Prestwich Bed 24; 35 m) is a heterolithic unit with lignites and *in situ* roots. A second leaf bed, in this case with leaves preserved as carbonised compressions, occurs near the base of the formation (locality 15.3).

The lower two-thirds of the next formation, the **Branksome Sand** (Prestwich Beds 25-27; about 65 m) comprises well-sorted sands exhibiting low angle cross-bedding or flat lamination. *Ophiomorpha* burrows occur in some beds. These sands are succeeded by 11 m of laminated muds with lignites and rootlets (locality 15.4) reminiscent of the Marsh Farm Formation lower down the succession. The remainder of the formation consists mainly of structureless muds.

Overall, the Bracklesham Group sequence in Alum Bay reflects the interplay between fluvial, coastal and marine processes. Marine horizons can be recognised by various criteria, the presence of glauconite and the trace fossil *Ophiomorpha* being the best field indicators. Transgressive events are marked by conglomerate bands overlying scoured surfaces, whilst well-sorted sands, such as those present in the lower part of the Branksome Sand, were deposited in a beach environment. The heterolithic facies, which characterises much of the Wittering Formation, appears to have been deposited close to the coastline in an intertidal flat situation. Some of the more lenticular sand bodies probably accumulated in tidal channels. The lignites, associated roots and palaeosols often associated with the heterolithic facies in the Marsh Farm Formation and at some other horizons represent coastal, slightly saline, marshes. Fluvial sedimentation is represented by the bulk of the Poole Formation, in which tabular and trough cross-bedded sands are associated with subordinate muds and conglomerates, in erosive-based and sometimes fining-upward sequences.

The Bracklesham Group is succeeded by the **Barton Group**, within which there are four formations. The lowest, the **Boscombe Sand** (Prestwich bed 28; 14 m), consists of a fine-grained, well-sorted sand. The base is gradational from the underlying Branksome Sand, while at the top the sand rapidly coarsens up into a thin conglomerate of large, rounded and battered flint pebbles which forms a prominent narrow ridge just south of the chair-lift (locality 15.5).

The **Barton Clay** (about 83 m) rests conformably on the conglomerate at the top of the Boscombe Sand. The lowest part of the formation consists of muds, lignitic and sandy near the base, and passes up through laminated muds into brown and green muds with a poorly preserved molluscan fauna. About 14 m above the base is a glauconitic sandy mud containing abundant *Nummulites* *prestwichianus.* Above the *N. prestwichianus* band, the remainder of the sequence consists of muds and sandy muds with some glauconitic beds and ironstone bands. Some horizons contain a rich molluscan fauna including *Athleta, Turritella, Crassatella* and *Corbula.* The succeeding 7 m of blue sandy clays with *Chama* and *Turritella,* formerly included within the Barton Clay, are now considered to be a separate formation, the **Chama Sand.**

The Chama Sand is overlain by the **Becton Sand** (formerly known as the Barton Sand or Headon Hill Sands; about 28 m). The junction is seen just north of Alum Bay Chine (locality 15.6), where the dip rapidly becomes nearly horizontal. This sudden change appears to be due to faulting, although the fault plane is obscure. The Becton Sand comprises white and pale yellow, well-sorted, fine-grained sands. There are no body fossils within the unit, but *Ophiomorpha* burrows occur in places.

Return to the car park via the steps at Alum Bay Chine or the chairlift. Alternatively, if time permits, continue northwards along the beach to Hatherwood Point where Itinerary 16 starts.

16. Headon Hill

The prime objective of this itinerary is to examine the type locality of the Headon Hill Formation and some of its constituent members. A variety of sedimentary facies is represented here, including good exposures of freshwater limestones and calcretes. The site is famous for its well preserved fossils. Molluscs are the most common macrofossils but vertebrates also occur, including fish, reptiles and mammals.

Vehicles may be parked in the car parks at the Needles Pleasure Park (306854), from which the beach is reached by descending the steps down Alum Bay Chine or, in the holiday season, by the chair lift. A path also descends from the customers' car park at the Headon Hall Tea Rooms (306857)(Figure 27), in which case permission should be sought or refreshments purchased! The itinerary involves a climb up and across rough and, in some places, fairly steep ground. After prolonged wet weather some parts of the section become impassable and care should be taken when crossing the various mudflows at all times. Total walking distance up to about 4 km.

References. Daley & Edwards (1974, 1990), Insole & Daley (1985), Paul (1989).

On reaching the beach, turn right and walk northwards to Hatherwood Point (305860) passing exposures in the Barton Group (see Itinerary 15). In the small

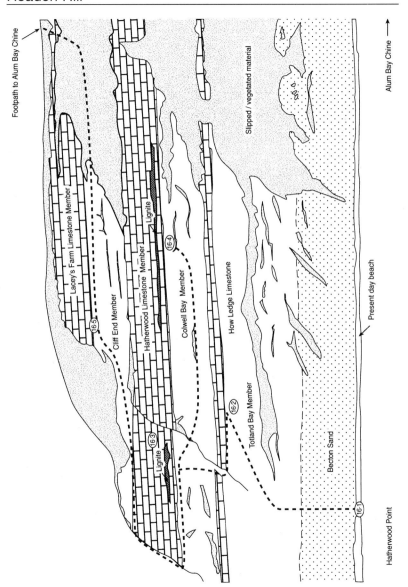

Figure 29. Field sketch of the western end of Headon Hill, including a suggested route.

bay just south of Hatherwood Point (locality 16.1), the general arrangement of the strata can be seen in the terraced cliff at the southern end of Headon Hill (Figure 29). From this point it is possible to ascend the cliff.

The base of the **Headon Hill Formation** may be visible at the top of the lowest scarp where brown muds with a sharp contact on the pale sands of the Becton Sand below. The lowest part of the formation, the **Totland Bay Member** (27 m), is poorly exposed, but comprises silty muds, marls, occasional sands and pale brown shelly limestones. The latter contain the freshwater pulmonate (air-breathing) gastropods *Galba* and *Planorbina*. The muds and marls range from those deposited in freshwater and containing gastropods such as *Viviparus* through to those laid down in brackish water situations and containing bivalves like *Corbicula*. Vertebrate fossils include fragments of freshwater turtle shells, crocodile teeth and the diamond-shaped scales of the gar fish *Lepidosteus*. The most conspicuous bed is the How Ledge Limestone (about 2 m) which is usually exposed at the rear of the first terrace slightly to the south of Hatherwood Point (locality 16.2). The top of the member is about 1 m above the top of the How Ledge Limestone.

The **Colwell Bay Member** (over 9 m) underlies the second terrace in the cliff. Although mostly obscured by mudflows, it is usually possible to trace the main features of the succession in the embayment just south of Hatherwood Point (locality 16.3). The basal Neritina Bed is a dark brown clayey sand which fills burrows in the underlying mud of the Totland Bay Member. It contains a rich fauna including *Corbicula, Potamides, Melanoides* and *Theodoxus*. The remainder of the unit comprises blue-green, grey and brown muds and muddy sands with *Batillaria, Potamides, Ostrea, Corbicula*, etc. If exposures are favourable, both the Venus Bed and the Colwell Oyster Bed can be seen. A thin limestone with *Galba* occurs near the top of the member. The uppermost 2 to 3 m consist of greenish interbedded fine sand and mud with bands of shells, especially *Batillaria* and *Potamides* (Batillaria Bed). Molluscan assemblages within the Colwell Bay Member often possess low species diversity while being rich in individuals and are dominated by cerithid gastropods (*Batillaria* and *Potamides*), oysters (*Ostrea*) and corbiculid bivalves (*Corbicula*). This indicates that the sequence was deposited in estuarine or lagoonal environments rather than under fully marine conditions. Some of the gastropod shells exhibit traces of the original colour pattern, a feature that is especially common in the case of *Theodoxus* shells in the Neritina Bed.

At this locality, the **Hatherwood Limestone Member** (up to 8 m) rests directly on the Colwell Bay Member, the sands of the **Linstone Chine Member** being thin to absent here, although well developed at the Totland Bay end of the hill. The Hatherwood Limestone Member forms a prominent scar towards the top of

Headon Hill

the seaward-facing cliff. It comprises pale, soft to well lithified, more or less fossiliferous limestones. At intervals through the succession, there are thin laminated crusts, associated with "pisolitic" bands, which are considered to have originated through calcretisation. This occurred during dry climatic phases when there was subaerial exposure and soil-forming processes operated. A discontinuous lignitic mud occurs about 2 m above the base. This can be seen above locality 16.3, but can more conveniently be examined about 50 m further south (locality 16.4). This Lignite Bed occurs above an irregular palaeotopographic surface on which clasts of limestone, some of boulder size, rest. This irregular topography resulted from a combination of karstic weathering and sapping of the underlying limestone to form potholes and collapse breccias.

The most common fossils within the Hatherwood Limestone Member are the freshwater pulmonate gastropods *Galba* and *Planorbina,* although some horizons, particularly higher up the sequence, contain brackish water forms such as *Nystia, Tarebia* and *Theodoxus.* The Lignite Bed yields vertebrates, including turtle and mammalian material.

The higher units of the succession can be reached by climbing the steep grassy ridge which forms the northern edge of the Hatherwood Limestone scarp above Hatherwood Point. The **Cliff End Member** (8·7 m) comprises variously coloured muds and marls with thin shell debris layers. It underlies the third terrace in the cliff and is poorly exposed. The **Lacey's Farm Limestone Member** forms the uppermost cliff on the hillside and is best seen at locality 16.5. Sandy muds with calcareous nodules occur at its base. The size and number of calcareous nodules increases upwards, so that there is a passage into a rubbly limestone with laminated crusts and "pisolitic" bands, probably representing a calcrete.

The overlying members of the Headon Hill Formation are poorly exposed above Hatherwood Point. The top of the hill is capped by sands and gravels of the Quaternary **Older River Gravels** (= Plateau Gravels), which can be seen in isolated exposures on the seaward side of Headon Warren.

From the cliff top at Hatherwood Point, it is possible to return to the car parks via a footpath over Headon Warren. Do not attempt to walk southwards along the cliff edge since there is no right of way in this direction.

If time permits, it is possible to continue the itinerary to examine lateral changes within the various stratigraphical units as well as younger horizons not exposed at Hatherwood Point. Whilst it is possible to do this by a traverse of the northern face of Headon Hill, the vegetational cover and slips may make progress difficult. It is, therefore, preferable to walk north-

eastwards along the coastal footpath over Headon Hill (Figure 27). Alternatively, drive from the car park to Cliff Road, Totland, where the coastal path can be reached at 319864. Car parking space here is limited to a single vehicle.

From the coastal path at about 318864, it is possible to reach the cliff edge and examine the upper part of the Headon Hill Formation, although access and exposure vary according to ground and weather conditions. Good exposures normally occur, for example, in the **Linstone Chine Member** (2·2 m) which comprises heterolithic fine sands and muds with ripple marks and small washouts.

At 317863, the **Bembridge Limestone** is accessible in an old quarry just below the top of the cliff. It may be possible to see the transitional relationship between the red and green mottled muds of the underlying **Osborne Marls Member** of the Headon Hill Formation and the Bembridge Limestone, there being a gradual increase in carbonate nodules upwards. The Bembridge Limestone here includes indurated masses of white limestone which are pisolitic and interpreted as calcretes. These limestones contain freshwater gastropods such as *Galba* and *Planorbina* plus a diverse fauna of terrestrial forms such as *Palaeoxestina, Megalocochlea* and *"Filholia"*. The top of the section contains lignitic muds within a sequence of soft marly limestones and marls. The contact of the Bembridge Limestone with the Bouldnor Formation is not exposed at this locality.

17. Colwell Bay

At Colwell Bay (Figure 30), a low cliff section, together with intermittent foreshore exposures, provides an opportunity to examine the lower part of the Headon Hill Formation. The section is particularly noteworthy for the presence of a very fossiliferous development of the Colwell Bay Member. Overall, it provides an interesting comparison with the succession seen on Headon Hill (Itinerary 16), from which it differs in a quite striking manner, and also with that at Whitecliff Bay (Itinerary 2).

The most convenient point of access is via Colwell Chine Road, at the seaward end of which is a public car park (327878). The section is accessible at most states of the tide but available foreshore exposures can only be examined at low tide. Access to part of the cliff may involve traversing an "apron" of fallen cliff debris. This should be undertaken with great care since such material may sometimes be very soft and it is all too easy to get stuck! Total walking distance about 2 km.

References. Daley & Edwards (1974), Insole & Daley (1985), Paul (1989), White (1921).

Colwell Bay

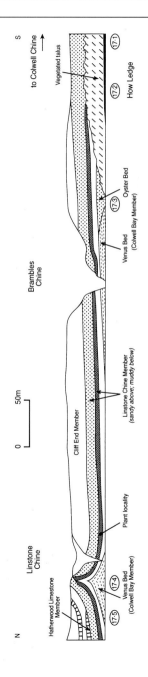

Figure 30. Cliff section in the Headon Hill Formation in Colwell Bay.

Colwell Bay

Descend shorewards and turn northwards along the top of the sea wall. The very low cliff immediately north of Colwell Chine (locality 17.1) exposes the How Ledge Limestone which lies close to the top of the **Totland Bay Member** of the **Headon Hill Formation.** This is a pale brown limestone containing the freshwater gastropods *Galba* and *Planorbina*. The northerly dip brings the limestone down to beach level at How Ledge, about 150 m further north.

The **Colwell Bay Member** (about 10 m) is poorly exposed in the cliffs near Colwell Chine, but from the middle of the bay northwards there is an excellent and continuous section. The base of the member is not normally visible in the cliff, but is occasionally exposed at low tide on the foreshore just north of How Ledge (locality 17.2). It consists of extremely shelly, blue muds (the Neritina Bed), which rest on and infill burrows in a grey mud belonging to the Totland Bay Member. The fauna of the Neritina Bed includes *Theodoxus concavus* (frequently with the original colour pattern preserved), *Potamides* and *Corbicula*.

In the cliff itself, the lowest bed exposed is the Venus Bed, comprising bioturbated blue sandy muds, with an abundant and diverse molluscan assemblage including the characteristic bivalve *Sinodia (= Venus) suborbicularis,* together with *Corbicula* and the gastropods *Globularia, Potamides* and *Pollia*. This unit was deposited within a hyposaline lagoon. The Venus Bed passes up into green bioturbated muds, overlain by a grey to green muddy sand with *Ostrea velata* (Colwell Oyster Bed). Along most of the section, the latter is less than 1 m thick, but between Colwell and Brambles Chines (locality 17.3), it thickens to about 3.5 m and cuts down into the Venus Bed. At this locality, it comprises a mass of oyster shells in a sandy matrix. As well as the dominant *Ostrea,* this bed contains *"Murex" sexdentatus* and *Nucula headonensis*. This oyster-rich lens represents a tidal channel-fill.
Near Brambles Chine, the Venus Bed is normally well exposed. Here, the abundant, diverse and predominantly marine fauna, includes paired valves of *Sinodia suborbicularis,* of which a large number are in life position. The Venus Bed also contains estuarine and a few freshwater forms, the latter apparently derived from the underlying Totland Bay Member. The remainder of the Colwell Bay Member here comprises green muddy sands and muds with a relatively sparse and restricted fauna, which includes *Potamides* and *Corbicula*. This part of the succession can be examined between Brambles and Linstone Chines.

The **Linstone Chine Member** (4 m) rests with a sharp and slightly undulose base on the preceding Colwell Bay Member. It can be seen capping the cliffs through much of the northern part of the bay, but can only be reached in the area north of Linstone Chine. This unit consists of pale brown or grey laminated silts and sands passing up into sands. Bands of the brackish water bivalve *Potamomya* occur near the base. The sands contain a variety of sedimentary structures including large- and small-scale cross-lamination (including the herringbone variety), and flaser bedding. They were probably deposited in an estuarine environment. Immediately north of Linstone Chine, the Linstone Chine Member and the upper part of the Colwell Bay Member are involved in a small anticlinal fold (locality 17.4). Plant macrofossils have been found in the vicinity of this fold.

Along most of the section, the Cliff End Member (seen to over 10 m) has a sharp, erosional contact with the underlying Linstone Chine Member. A patchy conglomerate of limestone and other clasts rests on this junction. The rest of the member consists mainly of muds and thin sands with shell bands in which *Corbicula, Potamomya* and *Potamides* occur. A thin pale brown limestone with *Galba* and *Planorbina* occurs about 3.5 m above the base of the member.

A significant feature of the section is the apparent absence of the **Hatherwood Limestone Member,** which is so well developed in Headon Hill a short distance to the south. However, at Cliff End, at the northern end of Colwell Bay (locality 17.5), the Linstone Chine Member passes up into a 0.5 m thick buff limestone with *Galba.* This appears to be the thin local representative of the Hatherwood Limestone Member. Its top is truncated by an erosion surface and there is no indication of the original thickness.

At Cliff End, the succession continues with the **Fishbourne Member** (3·0 m). This comprises greenish to grey muds with ferruginous concretions and lenticular bands with crushed *Viviparus, Melanopsis, Melanoides* and fish bones. The red and green, colour-mottled and essentially unfossiliferous **Osborne Marls Member** (about 13·5 m) completes the succession, the Lacey's Farm Limestone Member being absent here.

Do not attempt to continue northwards along the base of the cliff beyond Cliff End for this is private land. Return instead along the beach to Colwell Chine.

18. Bouldnor and Hamstead

The foreshore and intermittent cliff sections along the coast between Bouldnor and Hamstead (Figure 31) provide the only locality where the whole of the Bouldnor Formation may be examined. The Bembridge Marls Member and the lower part of the overlying Hamstead Member are best exposed in the cliff and foreshore section on the coast north of Hamstead (around 400918). The upper part of the formation, the Cranmore Member, is accessible at the top of the cliff northwest of Cranmore (386904). **Access to this area is not easy and it is preferable to divide the itinerary into two subsections, one looking at the foreshore and cliff exposures at the eastern end of the section and the second examining the upper part of the sequence in the cliffs at Cranmore. Both areas can be reached from the main A3054 Newport-Yarmouth road.**

Bouldnor and Hamstead

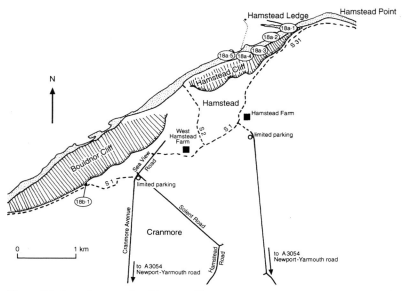

Figure 31. Location map for Itinerary 18.

References. Collinson (1983), Daley (1974), Daley & Edwards (1974), Insole & Daley (1985), White (1921).

18a Hamstead Ledge
Access is possible by car along the private road towards Hamstead Farm (400913). Some 50 m before the farm there is very limited parking. Permission to leave a vehicle here must be obtained from the farm or from Hamstead Grange. For larger parties (i.e. more than one car and minibuses), it is advisable to walk to Hamstead Farm after parking at the end of Cranmore Avenue (see Itinerary 18b below). From the farm, follow the footpath which descends to the shore. A southwesterly traverse is recommended, starting at Hamstead Point (406921). Extensive areas of the foreshore may be covered with shingle but this can sometimes form a thin veneer over very soft mud, so great care is necessary in crossing such areas. Total walking distance about 5 km.

Just to the west of the point, a low cliff (locality 18a.1) exhibits intermittent sections in the top of the **Bembridge Limestone.** The overlying **Bembridge Marls Member** (21·5 m) of the **Bouldnor Formation** (about 97 m) can be seen in the cliff section to the west, but is best examined at low water, preferably at the time of equinoctial spring tides, when a complete, unbroken succession is normally exposed (locality 18a.2).

The contact between the Bembridge Limestone and the Bembridge Marls Member is marked by a thin shell bed with *Ostrea* capping the underlying limestone. The lowest 4 m of the member consists of a sequence of predominantly black and grey to green muds and marls which contain a fauna dominated by brackish water molluscs, including *Corbicula, Polymesoda, Potamides, Melanoides* and *Mytilopsis*. Shells are well preserved in the grey and black muds and sometimes have pyritised surfaces. In contrast, in the green muds and marls the fossils are chalky and friable. The Insect Limestone is absent at this locality, but the unusual *Viviparus/Serpula* assemblage seen elsewhere occurs about 1 m above the base of the member. A metre or so higher are mottled brown and grey muds with ostracods concentrated on partings and in lenses. Both mud-cracked and burrowed surfaces are common in this part of the succession.

The remainder of the Bembridge Marls Member comprises a succession of muds and silty muds varying in colour from grey-green to black. Molluscan fossils are common throughout much of the sequence. They may occur in isolation, but are usually concentrated in thin bands or "partings", which may also contain vertebrate debris (mainly fish), some silt or fine sand. Such concentrations probably accumulated following storms or periods of greater water throughput. The frequent occurrence of *Viviparus* suggests a freshwater environment and that this sequence represents an overall regression. However, the presence of *Melanoides* and *Melanopsis* in some assemblages indicates that there were occasionally slightly higher salinities. A reversion to truly brackish salinities is indicated by a distinct 0·2 m thick shell band containing *Corbicula* and *Potamides,* a horizon recognisable within all the available Bembridge Marls Member exposures. The high-spired gastropod *Potamaclis* is common in the central part of the succession (locality 18a.3) and, on some bedding planes, the shells exhibit parallel orientation produced by current flow. In the same part of the sequence, between 70 and 125 m along the foreshore west of the junction with the Bembridge Limestone, there are a number of dark brown to black carbonaceous seams containing fruits, seeds and, less commonly, leaves. All the plants represented are aquatic or marginal aquatic forms. Rootlets and, in a few cases, roots are apparent *in situ* at some horizons. Various freshwater gastropods occur in association with the plant remains, including *Viviparus* and the pulmonates (air-breathers) *Galba* and *Planorbina.* Just below the top of the member is a distinctive 7 cm thick band comprising minute gastropods, the Nystia Band.

In the low coastal cliff 200 m east of the line of posts (locality 18a.4), the so-

Bouldnor and Hamstead

called Black Band (0.5 m) is exposed. This laterally extensive bed lies at the base of the **Hamstead Member**. It comprises a black carbonaceous mud with freshwater molluscs (*Viviparus, Unio*) and from which roots extend downwards into the underlying unit. The Black Band represents a shallow water marsh and marks a period of very slow sedimentation. Some workers take this horizon to mark the Eocene/Oligocene boundary.

Immediately west of the posts (locality 18a.5), the Nematura Bed (0.9 m) is exposed on the foreshore. It consists of dark grey-brown laminated clay with shelly seams containing brackish water fossils, including *Polymesoda, Nystia* and *Melanoides*. To the west, intermittent exposures of the Hamstead Member may occur at the base of the cliffs. Most of the sections reveal green muds resembling those of the underlying Bembridge Marls Member, with thin shell seams packed variously with *Galba, Planorbina, Viviparus, Melanoides, Unio* and *Polymesoda*. About 750 m west of the line of posts, in a small bay, a conspicuous sequence of white shell-debris beds interspersed with grey-green muds is usually visible near the base of the cliffs (locality 18a.6). This is the White Band (about 1·6 m), which lies about 20 m above the base of the Hamstead Member. The presence of molluscs, such as *Potamides* in this bed, indicates a temporary return to brackish water conditions. 20 m above the White Band is the Waterlily Bed (0·5 m), a laminated, carbonaceous mud with leaves, seeds and freshwater molluscs, such as *Unio* and *Viviparus*. However, since much of the sequence around this level within the Hamstead Member is usually obscured by mudflows and vegetation, it may not be possible to trace this unit.

From the centre of the bay, just west of a small hut, a path ascends the cliff and eventually joins the coastal path near Hamstead. This path can then be followed eastwards back to Hamstead Farm.

18b. Cranmore
Drive up Cranmore Avenue to the road junction at the top of the hill (390907) where there is very limited parking for vehicles. Cranmore Avenue is a private road and is unsuitable for coaches. From this point, follow the coastal footpath westwards towards Yarmouth. Just to the west of the point where the footpath reaches the coast, there is easy access to the upper part of the cliff (Figure 31). Large areas of the cliff here are affected to a greater or lesser extent by landslips and mudflows. Such areas are dangerous and should be treated with extreme caution, particularly after wet weather. Total walking distance about 2 km.

At the top of the cliff (locality 18b.1), the **Cranmore Member** (9·2 m)of the **Bouldnor Formation** is exposed beneath a thin capping of Quaternary **Older River Gravels** (= Plateau Gravels). The base of the member is marked by an abrupt change from a bright green to a brown-grey clay, the former being the highest bed of the Hamstead Member. The member is divided into the Corbula Beds (5·8 m) and the underlying Cerithium Beds (3·4 m). Both consist of brown weathering, very fossiliferous blue, grey and black muds. The Cerithium Beds contain mainly brackish water molluscs, such as *Pirenella monilifera, Nystia duchasteli* and *Polymesoda convexa,* but a few marine forms also occur. The overlying Corbula Beds contain more marine forms, including the gastropod *Volutispina (Athleta) rathieri* and the small bivalves *Corbula subpisum* and *Lentidium nitidium.*

The bulk of the cliff at this point consists of the **Hamstead Member.** This comprises mainly grey-green and green clays with occasional bands of dark brown or black laminated clays. However, much of the succession is obscured by slips and vegetation. **Return along the coastal footpath to the top of Cranmore Avenue.**

19. Thorness Bay and Gurnard

This itinerary covers the exposures of the Bouldnor Formation and the Bembridge Limestone in Thorness Bay and for a short distance to the north of Gurnard Ledge (Figure 32). The best known feature of this locality is the thin Bembridge Insect Bed which has yielded a prolific flora and insect fauna. Various macrofossil (mainly molluscan) assemblages representing brackish to freshwater environments also occur, whilst an unusual silicified development in the Bembridge Limestone contains pseudomorphs after gypsum.

The section is best approached from the northeast using the coastal footpath from Gurnard Bay. There is a limited amount of car parking space beside the road at the western end of Marsh Road, Gurnard (471953). This itinerary is best attempted on a falling tide since certain parts of it are inaccessible at high tide. Large areas of the cliffs are affected by mudflows and such areas should be treated with extreme caution, particularly after wet weather. Total walking distance about 8 km.

References. Armenteros *et al.* (1997), Daley (1972, 1973, 1974, 1989), Daley & Edwards (1974, 1990), Jarzembowski (1980), Reid & Chandler (1926).

Walk southwestwards from the road along the coastal footpath towards Thorness Bay. On the seaward side of the path there may be discontinuous exposures of southwesterly-dipping **Bembridge Limestone.** In the this area, this formation comprises upper and lower limestones separated by about 3 m of brown mud with *Corbicula* in a distinct dark band near the top. The limestones contain *Galba* and sometimes small hydrobiid gastropods and charophyte oögonia. At

Thorness Bay and Gurnard

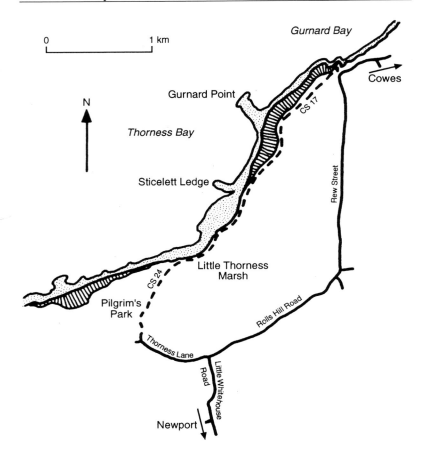

Figure 32. Location map for Itinerary 19.

beach level north of Gurnard Ledge, the lower limestone contains brown ferruginous cherts containing tiny silica pseudomorphs after gypsum.

Gurnard Ledge is formed by the lower limestone unit of the Bembridge Limestone. Immediately south of the ledge, at 464945, the sharp, irregular and burrowed junction with the **Bembridge Marls Member** (21·5 m) of the overlying **Bouldnor Formation** can be seen. The overlying grey muds with shell bands (0·7 m) contain a restricted brackish water fauna including corbiculid bivalves, *Potamides, Melanoides* and *Ostrea.*

About 0·9 m above the base of the member is a laterally variable argillaceous band, some 0·8 m thick. It comprises dark blue-grey laminated mud with two or more discontinuous bands and lenses of distinctive, buff, blue-hearted, fine-grained limestone and marl. This is the Bembridge Insect Bed and the limestone within it has yielded over 200 species of insects, a diverse flora and other delicate fossils, including bird feathers. Unfortunately, these fossils are apparently not as common as they were in the past.

The next few metres above the Bembridge Insect Bed consist of grey to blue-green muds, marls and a thin limestone containing large numbers of brackish water molluscs. The assemblages have a low diversity, *Polymesoda convexa* and *Melanoides acuta* being the most common, with smaller numbers of *Corbicula, Mytilopsis, Mytilus, Potamomya* and *Potamides.* The shells are mostly concentrated into bands, but some are more randomly distributed with some of the bivalves occurring in life position. One horizon contains an unusual assemblage comprising "knots" of the calcareous worm tube *"Serpula",* *Melanoides* and the freshwater snail *Viviparus.* Preservation varies according to the lithology: grey muds contain well-preserved fossils, whilst in the green muds and marls, shells are chalky and friable, sometimes only occurring as moulds.

Higher in the succession, come muds and marls containing freshwater assemblages, including the molluscs *Viviparus, Galba* and *Planorbina,* together with plant seeds. Plant leaves have been found in clay ironstone concretions which occur at some horizons. Near the top of the cliff, a thin sequence of the **Hamstead Member** with the Black Band at the base, may be visible.

South of Gurnard Ledge, the cliff becomes lower towards Little Thorness Marsh (459936), where the beds have been disturbed by recent rotational slipping. In the centre of the Thorness Bay, the Palaeogene is obscured by modern beach sediment, but reappears in the very low cliff northeast of Pilgrims Park (454934).

If the state of the tide is suitable, continue southwestwards to below Thorness Wood (449933), where the best section in the southern part of the bay occurs. The upper part of the Bembridge Marls Member and a possible outcrop of the overlying Hamstead Member are obscured by vegetation and slips, but good exposures of the lower part of the former occur at the base of the cliff and on the foreshore at low tide.

Almost 15 m of shelly muds, marls and a few thin limestones are present above a *Serpula*-bearing bed similar to that seen near Gurnard Ledge. Low diversity brackish water molluscan assemblages, with *Polymesoda, Mytilopsis, Potamomya* and *Melanoides,* are common in the lowest 5 m of the succession. Some bivalves occur in life position, but most of the fossils are concentrated into

Thorness Bay and Gurnard

bands or partings. Fossil algae with well-preserved filaments form thin crusts on the upper surfaces of the molluscs, particularly the convex-up bivalves.

Higher up, the succession comprises muds and silty muds containing freshwater gastropods, such as *Viviparus* and *Planorbina,* but other gastropods include *Potamaclis* and *Melanopsis,* the latter perhaps suggesting slightly raised salinities from time to time. A distinctive shell band containing *Corbicula,* as double valves, and *Potamides* records a more pronounced, although temporary, incursion of brackish water into the area. The cliff section also has some interesting sedimentological features. Some horizons exhibit varve-like graded laminae with truncating scours and gutter structures. One horizon just over 2 m below the *Corbicula* band has a distinct pattern of sediment-filled polygonal cracks. Whether these are true desiccation cracks is open to question.

Intermittent sections occur further west, but much of the section is obscured. It is, therefore, advisable to return to Gurnard Bay via the coastal path. Alternatively, if transport arrangements allow and permission is obtained, it is possible to be picked up from the private road which reaches the foreshore via the holiday camp at Pilgrims Park.

FURTHER READING

ALLEN, D.J. & HOLLOWAY, S. 1984. *Investigation of the Geothermal Potential of the UK: The Wessex* Basin. British Geological Survey, 80pp.

ARMENTEROS, I., DALEY, B. & GARCIA, E. 1997. Lacustrine and palustrine facies in the Bembridge Limestone (late Eocene, Hampshire Basin) of the Isle of Wight, southern England. *Palaeogeography, Palaeoclimatology, Palaeoecology,* **128,** 111-132.

BASFORD, H.V. 1980. *The Vectis Report: A Survey of Isle of Wight Archaeology.* Isle of Wight County Council, vi + 172pp.

BEVAN, T.G. & HANCOCK, P.L. 1986. A late Cenozoic regional mesofracture system in southern England and northern France. *Journal of the Geological Society, London,* **143,** 355-362.

BEVAN, T.G. & HANCOCK, P.L. 1987. Brittle modes of foreland extension. In M.P. Coward, J.F. Dewey, & P.L. Hancock (eds.). *Continental Extensional Tectonics,* Geological Society Special Publication No. 28, 127-137.

BIRPS & ECORS. 1986. Deep seismic reflection profiling between England, France and Ireland. *Journal of the Geological Society, London,* **143,** 45-52.

BRISTOW, H.W., REID, C. & STRACHAN, A., 1889. The geology of the Isle of Wight (2nd edition). *Memoir. Geological Survey of the United Kingdom,* xiv + 349pp.

BROMHEAD, E.N., CHANDLER, M.P. & HUTCHINSON, J.N. 1991. The recent history and geotechnics of landslides at Gore Cliff, Isle of Wight. *In International Conference on Slope Stability Engineering - Developments and Applications.* Thomas Telford, London, 189-195.

BUURMAN, P. 1980. Palaeosols in the Reading Beds (Paleocene) of Alum Bay, Isle of Wight, U.K. *Sedimentology,* **27,** 593-606.

CASEY, R. 1961. The stratigraphical palaeontology of the Lower Greensand. *Palaeontology,* **3,** 487-621.

CHADWICK, R.A. 1985a. Permian, Mesozoic and Cenozoic structural evolution of England and Wales in relation to the principles of extension and inversion tectonics. *In* A. Whittaker (ed.) *Atlas of Onshore Sedimentary Basins in England and Wales: Post-Carboniferous Tectonics and Stratigraphy.* Blackie, Glasgow & London, 9-25.

CHADWICK, R.A. 1985b. End Jurassic-early Cretaceous sedimentation and subsidence (late Portlandian to Barremian) and the late Cimmerian unconformity. *In* A. Whittaker (ed.) *Atlas of Onshore Sedimentary Basins in England and Wales: Post-Carboniferous Tectonics and Stratigraphy.* Blackie, Glasgow & London, 52-56.

CHADWICK, R.A. 1985c. Cenozoic sedimentation, subsidence and tectonic inversion. *In* A. Whittaker (ed.) *Atlas of Onshore Sedimentary Basins in England and Wales: Post-Carboniferous Tectonics and Stratigraphy.* Blackie, Glasgow & London, 61-63.

Further Reading

CHADWICK, R.A. 1986. Extension tectonics in the Wessex Basin, southern England. *Journal of the Geological Society, London,* **143**, 465-488.

CHADWICK, R.A. 1991. Aspects of basin inversion in southern Britain. *Journal of the Geological Society, London,* **150**, 311-322.

CHADWICK, R.A., KENOLTY, N. & WHITTAKER, A. 1983. Crustal structure beneath southern England from deep seismic reflection profiles. *Journal of the Geological Society, London,* **140**, 898-911.

CHANDLER, M.P. & HUTCHINSON, J.N. 1982. Assessment of relative slide hazard within a large, pre-existing coastal landslide at Ventnor, Isle of Wight. *IV International Symposium on Landslides, Toronto,* **2**, 517-522.

CLIFFORD, H.J. 1936. A Mesolithic flora in the Isle of Wight. *Proceedings of the Isle of Wight Natural History and Archaeological Society,* **2**, 582-594.

CLIFTON, H.E., HUNTER, R.E. & PHILLIPS, R.L. 1971. Depositional structures and processes in the non-barred, high-energy nearshore. *Journal of Sedimentary Petrology,* **41**, 651-670.

CODRINGTON, T. 1870. On the superficial deposits of the south of Hampshire and the Isle of Wight. *Quarterly Journal of the Geological Society. London,* **26**, 528-551.

COLENUTT, G.W. 1929. The cliff-founder and landslide at Gore Cliff, Isle of Wight. *Proceedings of the Isle of Wight Natural History and Archaeological Society,* **1**, 561-570.

COLLINSON, M.E. 1983. Palaeofloristic assemblages and palaeoecology of the Lower Oligocene Bembridge Marls, Hamstead Ledge, Isle of Wight. *Botanical Journal of the Linnean Society,* **86**, 177-225.

CRANE, P.R. 1977. The Alum Bay plant beds. *Tertiary Research,* **1**, 95-99.

CRITTENDEN, S. 1983. A foraminiferal analysis of the Atherfield Clay (Lower Aptian) of the Isle of Wight, UK, with special emphasis on the arenaceous aspects. *In* J.G. Verdenius, J.E. van Hinte & A.R. Fortuin (eds.). *Proceedings of the First Workshop on Arenaceous Foraminifera.* Continental Shelf Institute, Norway, Publication No. 108, 9-30.

DALEY, B. 1972. Macroinvertebrate assemblages from the Bembridge Marls (Oligocene) of the Isle of Wight, England and their environmental significance. *Palaeogeography, Palaeoclimatology, Palaeoecology,* **11**, 11-32.

DALEY, B. 1973. The palaeoenvironment of the Bembridge Marls (Oligocene) of the Isle of Wight. *Proceedings of the Geologists' Association,* **84**, 83-93.

DALEY, B. 1974. Shell encrusting algae from the Bembridge Marls (Lattorfian) of the Isle of Wight, Hampshire, England. *Revue de Micropaléontologie. Paris,* **17**, 15-22.

DALEY, B. 1989. Silica pseudomorphs from the Bembridge Limestone (Upper Eocene) of the Isle of Wight, southern England, and their palaeoclimatic significance. *Palaeogeography, Palaeoclimatology, Palaeoecelogy,* **69**, 233-240.

DALEY, B. & EDWARDS, N. 1971. Palaeogene warping in the Isle of Wight. *Geological Magazine,* **108**, 399-405.

Further Reading

DALEY, B. & EDWARDS, N. 1974. Weekend Field Meeting: The Upper Eocene-Lower Oligocene Beds of the Isle of Wight. *Proceedings of the Geologists' Association,* **85,** 281-292.

DALEY, B. & EDWARDS, N. 1990. The Bembridge Limestone (Late Eocene), Isle of Wight, southern England: a stratigraphical revision. *Tertiary Research,* **12,** 51-64.

DALEY, B. & STEWART, D.J. 1979. Weekend Field Meeting: The Wealden Group in the Isle of Wight. *Proceedings of the Geologists' Association,* **90,** 51-54.

DEVOY, R.J. 1987. The estuary of the Western Yar, Isle of Wight: sea-level changes in the Solent region. In K.E. Barber (ed.). *Wessex and the Isle of Wight - Field Guide,* Quaternary Research Association, Cambridge, 115-122.

DIKE, E.F. 1972a. *Sedimentology of the Lower Greensand of the Isle of Wight.* Unpublished D.Phil. thesis, University of Oxford.

DIKE, E.F. 1972b. *Ophiomorpha nodosa* Lundgren. Environmental implications in the Lower Greensand of the Isle of Wight. *Proceedings of the Geologists' Association,* **83,** 165-177.

DYER, K.R. 1975. The buried channels of the 'Solent River', southern England. *Proceedings of the Geologists' Association,* **86,** 239-245.

EATON, G.L. 1976. Dinoflagellate cysts from the Bracklesham Beds (Eocene) of the Isle of Wight, southern England. *Bulletin of the British Museum (Natural History) (Geology),* **26,** 227-332.

EDWARDS, R.A. & FRESHNEY, E.C. 1987. Lithostratigraphical classification of the Hampshire Basin Palaeogene deposits (Reading Formation to Headon Formation). *Tertiary Research,* **8,** 43-73.

EDWARDS, R.A. & FRESHNEY, E.C. 1987. *Geology of the country around Southampton. Memoir for 1:50 000 geological sheet 315 (England & Wales).* British Geological Survey, x + 111pp.

ENGLEFIELD, H.C. 1816. *A Description of the Principal Picturesque Beauties, Antiquities, and Geological Phaenomena of the Isle of Wight, with Additional Observations on the Strata of this Island, and their continuation in the Adjacent Parts of Dorsetshire, by Thomas Webster.* London.

EVERARD, C.E. 1954. The Solent River: a geomorphological study. *Transactions of the Institute of British Geographers,* **20,** 4-58.

FALCON, N.L. & KENT, P.C. 1960. Geological results of petroleum exploration in Britain, 1945-1957. *Geological Society of London, Memoir,* **2,** 1-56.

FISHER, O. 1862. On the Bracklesham Bay Beds of the Isle of Wight Basin. *Quarterly Journal of the Geological Society. London,* **18,** 65-94.

FITTON, W.H. 1847. A stratigraphical account from Atherfield to Rocken End, on the south-west coast of the Isle of Wight. *Quarterly Journal of the Geological Society. London,* **3,** 289-327.

FORBES, E. 1853. On the Tertiary Fluvio-Marine Formation of the Isle of Wight. *Quarterly Journal of the Geological Society of London,* **9,** 259-270.

Further Reading

GALE, A.S. & CLEEVELEY, R.J. 1989. Arthur Rowe and the zones of the White Chalk of the English coast. *Proceedings of the Geologists' Association,* **100,** 419-431.

GALE, A.S., HUGGETT, J.M. & GILL, M. 1996. The stratigraphy and petrography of the Gault Clay Formation (Albian, Cretaceous) at Redcliff, Isle of Wight. *Proceedings of the Geologists' Association,* **107,** 287-298.

GALE, A.S., WOOD, C.J. & BROMLEY, R.G. 1987. The lithostratigraphy and marker bed correlation of the White Chalk (Late Cenomanian - Campanian) of southern England. *Mesozoic Research,* **1,** 107-118.

GARDEN, I.R. 1991. Changes in the provenance of pebbly detritus in southern Britain and northern France associated with basin rifting. *In* A.C. Morton, S.P. Todd & P.D. Haughton (eds.). *Developments in Sedimentary Provenance,* Geological Society, London Special Publication No. 57, 273-289.

GOLDRING, R. & POLLARD, J.E. 1995. A re-evaluation of *Ophiomorpha* burrows in the Wealden Group (Lower Cretaceous) of southern England. *Cretaceous Research,* **16,** 665-680.

HODSON, F. & WEST, I.M. 1972. The Holocene deposits of Fawley, Hampshire and the development of Southampton Water. *Proceedings of the Geologists' Association,* **83,** 421-444.

HOLYOAK, D.T. & PREECE, R.C. 1983. Evidence of a high Middle Pleistocene sea-level from estuarine deposits at Bembridge, Isle of Wight, England. *Proceedings of the Geologists' Association,* **94,** 231-244.

HOWARD, J.D., FREY, R.W. & REINECK, H.E. 1972. Introduction. *Senckenbergiana Marina,* **4,** 3-14.

HOWARD, J.D. & REINECK, H.E., 1981. Depositional facies of high-energy beach-to-offshore sequence, comparison with low energy sequence. *Bulletin of the American Association of Petroleum Geologists,* **65,** 807-830.

HUTCHINSON, J.N. 1965. A reconnaissance of coastal landslides in the Isle of Wight. *Building Research Station, Note no. EN11/65.*

HUTCHINSON, J.N. 1984. Landslides in Britain and their countermeasures. *Journal of Japan Landslide Society,* **21,** 1-25.

HUTCHINSON, J.N. 1987. Some coastal landslides of the southern Isle of Wight. In K.E. Barber (ed.). *Wessex and the Isle of Wight - Field Guide,* Quaternary Research Association, Cambridge, 123-135.

HUTCHINSON, J.N. 1991. The landslides forming the south Wight Undercliff. *In International Conference on Slope Stability Engineering - Developments and Applications.* Thomas Telford, London, 157-168.

HUTCHINSON, J.N., BROMHEAD, E.N. & CHANDLER, M.P. 1991. Investigations of landslides at St. Catherine's Point, Isle of Wight. *In International Conference on Slope Stability Engineering - Developments and Applications.* Thomas Telford, London, 169-179.

Further Reading

HUTCHINSON, J.N., BRUNSDEN, D. & LEE, E.M. 1991. The geomorphology of the landslide complex at Ventnor, Isle of Wight. *In International Conference on Slope Stability Engineering - Developments and Applications.* Thomas Telford, London, 213-218.

HUTCHINSON, J.N., CHANDLER, M.P. & BROMHEAD, E.N. 1981. Cliff recession on the Isle of Wight SW coast. *In Proceedings, 10th International Conference of Soil Mechanics and Foundation Engineering,* Stockholm, Sweden, June 15-19, **1,** 429-434.

INSOLE, A.N. & DALEY, B. 1985. A revision of the lithostratigraphical nomenclature of the Late Eocene and Early Oligocene strata of the Hampshire Basin, southern England. *Tertiary Research,* **7,** 67-100.

INSOLE, A.N. & HUTT, S. 1994. The palaeoecology of the dinosaurs of the Wessex Formation (Wealden Group, early Cretaceous), Isle of Wight, southern England. *Zoological Journal of the Linnean Society,* **112,** 197-215.

JARZEMBOWSKI, E.A. 1980. Fossil insects from the Bembridge Marls, Palaeogene of the Isle of Wight, southern England. *Bulletin of the British Museum (Natural History) (Geology),* **33,** 237-293.

JEFFERIES, R.P.S. 1963. The stratigraphy of the *Actinocamax plenus* Subzone (Turonian) in the Anglo-Paris Basin. *Proceedings of the Geologists' Association,* **74,** 1-33.

KENNEDY, W.J. 1969. The correlation of the Lower Chalk of south-east England. *Proceedings of the Geologists' Association,* **80,** 459-560.

KENOLTY, N., CHADWICK, R.A., BLUNDELL, D.J. & BACON, M. 1981. Deep seismic reflection survey across the Variscan Front in southern England. *Nature, London,* **292,** 451-453.

KING, C. 1981. The stratigraphy of the London Clay and associated deposits. *Tertiary Research Special Paper,* **6,** 1-158.

LAKE, S.D. & KARNER, G.D. 1987. The structure and evolution of the Wessex Basin, southern England: an example of inversion tectonics. *Tectonophysics,* **137,** 347-378.

LIENGJARERN, M., COSTA, L. & DOWNIE, C. 1980. Dinoflagellate cysts from the Upper Eocene-Lower Oligocene of the Isle of Wight. *Palaeontology,* **23,** 475-499.

LORD, A.R. & BOWN, P.R.(eds.) 1987. *Mesozoic and Cenozoic Stratigraphical Micropalaeontology of the Dorset Coast and Isle of Wight, Southern England.* British Micropalaeontological Society, v + 183pp.

LOVEDAY, J. 1960. Plateau deposits of the southern Chiltern Hills. *Proceedings of the Geologists' Association,* **73,** 83-101.

MELVILLE, R.V. & FRESHNEY, E.C. 1982. The Hampshire Basin and adjoining areas. *British Regional Geology,* H.M.S.O. London, 4th edition, 146pp.

MIDDLEMISS, F.A. 1962. Brachiopod ecology and Lower Greensand palaeogeography. *Palaeontology,* **5,** 253-267.

Further Reading

MITCHELL, G.F., PENNY, L.F., SHOTTON, F.W. & WEST, R.G. 1973. *A Correlation of Quaternary Deposits in the British Isles.* Geological Society, London, Special Report, **4**, 1-99.

MORRIS, K. 1979. A classification of Jurassic marine shale sequences; an example from the Toarcian (Lower Jurassic) of Great Britain. *Palaeogeography, Palaeoclimatology, Palaeoecology,* **26**, 117-126.

MUNT, M.C. & BURKE, A. 1987. The Pleistocene geology and faunas at Newtown, Isle of Wight. *Proceedings of the Isle of Wight Natural History and Archaeological Society,* **8**, 7-14 (for 1986).

MURRAY, J.W. & WRIGHT, C.A. 1974. Palaeogene Foraminiferida and palaeoecology, Hampshire and Paris Basins, and the English Channel. *Special Papers in Palaeontology,* **14**, 129pp.

NICHOLLS, R.J. 1987. Evolution of the upper reaches of the Solent River and the formation of Poole and Christchurch Bays. In K.E. Barber (ed.). *Wessex and the Isle of Wight - Field Guide,* Quaternary Research Association, Cambridge, 99-114.

NIO, SWEI-DJIN. 1976. Marine transgressions as a factor in the formation of sandwave complexes. *Geologie en Mijnbouw,* **55**, 18-40.

OWEN, H.G. 1971. Middle Albian stratigraphy in the Anglo-Paris Basin. *Bulletin of the British Museum (Natural History) (Geology),* **Supplement. 8,** 164pp.

PARKES, D.A. & RENDELL, H.M. 1988. TL dating of brickearths from S.E. England. *Quaternary Science Review,* **7**, 305-308.

PAUL, C.R.C. 1989. The molluscan faunal succession in the Hatherwood Limestone Member (Upper Eocene), Isle of Wight, England. *Tertiary Research,* **10**, 147-162.

PENN, I.E. 1985. Some aspects of the deep geology of southern England and their bearing on the deep geology of France. *Documents du Bureau de Recherches Géologiques et Minières,* **95-12,** 1-28.

PLINT, A.G. 1982. Eocene sedimentation and tectonics in the Hampshire Basin. *Journal of the Geological Society,* **139**, 249-254.

PLINT, A.G. 1983. Facies, environments and sedimentary cycles in the Middle Eocene, Bracklesham Formation of the Hampshire Basin: evidence for global sea-level changes. *Sedimentology,* **30**, 625-653.

PREECE, R.C. 1980. The biostratigraphy and dating of a slope deposit on Gore Cliff, near Blackgang, Isle of Wight. *Journal of Archaeological Science,* **7**, 255-265.

PREECE, R.C. 1986. Faunal remains from radiocarbon-dated soils within landslip debris from The Undercliff, Isle of Wight. *Journal of Archaeological Science,* **13**, 189-200.

PREECE, R.C. 1987. Biostratigraphy and environmental archaeology of the post-glacial slope deposit on Gore Cliff, Isle of Wight. *In* K.E. Barber (ed.). *Wessex and the Isle of Wight - Field Guide.* Quaternary Research Association, Cambridge, 150-155.

Further Reading

PREECE, R.C. & SCOURSE, J.D. 1987. Pleistocene sea-level history in the Bembridge area of the Isle of Wight. *In* K.E. Barber (ed.), *Wessex and the Isle of Wight - Field Guide.* Quaternary Research Association, Cambridge, 136-149.

PREECE, R.C., SCOURSE, J.D., HOUGHTON, S.D., KNUDSEN, K.L. & PENNEY, D.N. 1990. The Pleistocene sea-level and neotectonic history of the eastern Solent, southern England. *Philosophical Transactions of the Royal Society of London,* **B328,** 425-477.

PRESTWICH, J. 1846. On the Tertiary or Supracretaceous Formations of the Isle of Wight as exhibited in the sections at Alum Bay and Whitecliff Bay. *Quarterly Journal of the Geological Society, London,* **2,** 223-259.

RADLEY, J.D. 1993. A derived Lower Jurassic clast from the Wealden Group (Lower Cretaceous) of the Isle of Wight, southern England. *Proceedings of the Geologists' Association,* **104,** 71-73.

RADLEY, J.D. 1994a. Field Meeting, 24-5 April, 1993: the Lower Cretaceous of the Isle of Wight. *Proceedings of the Geologists' Association,* **105,** 145-152.

RADLEY, J.D. 1994b. Stratigraphy, palaeontology and palaeoenvironment of the Wessex Formation (Wealden Group, Lower Cretaceous) at Yaverland, Isle of Wight, southern England. *Proceedings of the Geologists' Association,* **105,** 199-208.

RADLEY, J.D. 1995. Foraminifera from the Vectis Formation (Wealden Group, Lower Cretaceous) of the Wessex Sub-basin, southern England: a preliminary account. *Cretaceous Research,* **16,** 717-726.

REID, C. 1902. Geology of the Country around Ringwood. *Memoir. Geological Survey of Great Britain.*

REID, E.M. & CHANDLER, M.E.J. 1926. *The Bembridge Flora.* Catalogue of Cainozoic Plants in the Department of Geology, 1, British Museum (Natural History), London.

REINECK, H.E. & SINGH, I.B. 1980. *Depositional Sedimentary Environments - with Reference to Terrigenous Clastics.* Springer-Verlag, Berlin, 549pp. (2nd. edition).

RENDEL GEOTECHNICS. 1994. Blackgang, Isle of Wight: Assessment of Landslide Management Options. Rendel Geotechnics Report No. R/H366/1 for South Wight Borough Council, 27pp.

ROWE, A.W. 1908. The zones of the White Chalk of the English Coast, V, The Isle of Wight. *Proceedings of the Geologists' Association,* **20,** 209-352.

RUFFELL, A.H. 1988. Palaeoecology and event stratigraphy of the Wealden-Lower Greensand transition in the Isle of Wight. *Proceedings of the Geologists' Association,* **99,** 133-140.

RUFFELL, A.H. & HARVEY, M. 1993. Field excursion to the Cretaceous and Cenozoic of Redcliff (Sandown) and Whitecliff Bay, Isle of Wight, 5th January 1992. *Proceedings of the Ussher Society,* **8,** 77-78.

SCAIFE, R.G. 1987. The late Devensian and Flandrian vegetation of the Isle of Wight. *In* K.E. Barber (ed.), *Wessex and the Isle of Wight - Field Guide.* Quaternary Research Association, Cambridge, 156-180.

Further Reading

SELLWOOD, B.W. & SCOTT, J. 1986. A geological map of the sub-Mesozoic floor beneath southern England. *Proceedings of the Geologists' Association,* **97,** 81-85.

SHACKLETON, N.J., BERGER, A. & PELTIER, W.R. 1991. An alternative astronomical calibration of the lower Pleistocene timescale based on ODP Site 677. *Transactions of the Royal Society of Edinburgh,* **81,** 252-261.

SIMPSON, M.I 1985. The stratigraphy of the Atherfield Clay Formation (Lower Aptian, Lower Cretaceous) at the type and other localities in southern England. *Proceedings of the Geologists' Association,* **96,** 23-45.

SMITH, N.J.P. 1986. The pre-Permian subcrop map. In A. Whittaker (ed.) *Atlas of Onshore Sedimentary Basins in England and Wales: Post-Carboniferous Tectonics and Stratigraphy.* Blackie, Glasgow & London, 6-8.

STEWART, D.J. 1981a. A meander-belt sandstone of the Lower Cretaceous of southern England. *Sedimentology,* **28,** 1-20.

STEWART, D.J. 1981b. A field guide to the Wealden Group of the Hastings area and the Isle of Wight. *In International Fluvial Conference (Keele 1981),* Field Guide, Chapter 3, 3.1-3.31.

STEWART, D.J. 1983. Possible suspended-load channel deposits from the Wealden Group (Lower Cretaceous) of southern England. *Special Publication of the International Association of Sedimentologists,* **6,** 369-384.

STEWART, D.J., RUFFELL, A., WACH, G. & GOLDRING, R. 1991. Lagoonal sedimentation and fluctuating salinities in the Vectis Formation (Wealden Group, Lower Cretaceous) of the Isle of Wight, southern England. *Sedimentary Geology,* **72,** 117-134.

STINTON, F.C. 1971. Easter Field Meeting in the Isle of Wight. *Proceedings of the Geologists' Association,* **82,** 403-410.

STONELEY, R. 1982. The structural development of the Wessex Basin. *Journal of the Geological Society, London,* **139,** 543-554.

WACH, G.D. & RUFFELL, A.H. 1991. *The sedimentology and sequence stratigraphy of a Lower Cretaceous tide and storm-dominated clastic succession, Isle of Wight and S.E. England.* Field Trip B-16, 31 August-4 September, 1990, XIIIth Congress, International Association of Sedimentologists, Nottingham., England, 95pp.

WEST, R.G. 1972. Relative land-sea-level changes in southeastern England during the Pleistocene. *Philosophical Transactions of the Royal Society of London,* **A272,** 87-97.

WEST, I.M. 1980. Geology of the Solent estuarine system. *In The Solent Estuarine System.* NERC Publication, Series C. No. 22, 6-19.

WHITE, H.J.O. 1921. A short account of the geology of the Isle of Wight. *Memoir. Geological Survey of Great Britain,* viii + 235pp. (reprinted 1990).

WHITTAKER, A. 1986. The deep geological structure and evolution of southern Britain. *Proceedings of the Ussher Society.,* **6,** 291-298.

Further Reading

WHITTAKER, A. & CHADWICK, R.A. 1984. The large-scale structure of the Earth's crust beneath southern Britain. *Geological Magazine,* **121,** 621-624.

WHITTAKER, A., CHADWICK, R.A. & PENN, I.E. 1986. Deep crustal traverse across southern Britain from seismic reflection profiles. *Bulletin de la Societe Geologique de France,* (II) **8,** 55-68.

WOOLDRIDGE, S.W. & LINTON, D.L. 1955. *Structure, Surface and Drainage in South-East England.* Philip, viii + 176pp. (reprinted 1964).

ZIEGLER, P.A. 1981. Evolution of sedimentary basins in north-west Europe. *In* L.V. Illing & G.D. Hobson, (eds.). *Petroleum Geology of the Continental Shelf of North-West Europe.* Heyden, London, 3-39.

Association Guides

GEOLOGISTS' ASSOCIATION GUIDES

All the following are available from **Geological Society Publishing House, Unit 7, Brassmill Enterprise Centre, Brassmill Lane, Bath, BA1 3JN.** Credit card orders are accepted by telephone or fax. Tel: 01225 445046. Fax: 01225 442836.

No 2   The Lake District 1990
No 7   Geology of Manchester Area 1991
No 22 Dorset 1993
No 32 Isle of Arran 1989
No 34 Yorkshire Coast 1992
No 42 Mallorca 1990
No 43 Costa Blanca 1990
No 44 Late Precambrian Geology Scottish Highlands and Islands 1991
No 46 Isle of Man 1993
No 19 West Cornwall 1994
No 49 Tenerife 1994
No 53 Eastern & Central Jamaica 1995

No 47 Coastal Landforms of West Dorset 1992
No 50 Southern Cyprus 1994
No 51 The Island of Bute 1995
No 52 Iceland 1994
No 54 Aberystwyth District 1995
No 55 Early Cretaceous Environments of the Weald 1996
No 56 The Castleton Area – Derbyshire 1996
No 57 The Chalk of Sussex and Kent 1997
No 59 The Geology of Hadrian's Wall 1997